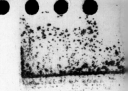

PROGRAMMED
BEGINNING ALGEBRA

UNIT V **Fractions and Fractional Equations**

IRVING DROOYAN & WILLIAM WOOTON

Pierce College, Los Angeles

JOHN WILEY AND SONS, INC. NEW YORK · LONDON

Copyright © 1963

by

John Wiley & Sons, Inc.

Library of Congress Catalog Card Number: 63-11429

Printed in the United States of America

Programmed Beginning Algebra consists of eight units of material, covering topics normally a part of a course in first-year algebra. The material is organized as follows:

Volume I { Unit I Natural Numbers
Unit II Integers

Volume II { Unit III First-Degree Equations and Inequalities in One Variable
Unit IV Products and Factors

Volume III Unit V Fractions and Fractional Equations

Volume IV Unit VI Graphs and Linear Systems

Volume V { Unit VII Radicals
Unit VIII Quadratic Equations

This program can be used in a variety of ways. For reasonably capable students who accomplish the entire program, it constitutes a complete first-year course in algebra. Preferably, the program should be supplemented with periodic classroom sessions or individual conferences with a qualified mathematics instructor; but, even without such assistance, a conscientious student can expect to achieve a degree of proficiency adequate to perform in a satisfactory manner on most standard achievement tests in beginning algebra.

Any one of the eight units can be used independently of the others. Each unit can be used as a self-tutor, to supplement and/or reinforce the same topic in any standard first-year algebra textbook. If classroom attendance is interrupted due to illness or for some other reason, the material missed in class can be covered by accomplishing the appropriate unit in this series. The statement of objectives and the table of contents at the beginning of each unit will give a good picture of the material covered herein.

The material, as presented, is somewhat modern in point of view. Set terminology and set symbolism are used where helpful, inequalities in one and two variables are discussed in conjunction with equations, solution sets of equations and their graphs are approached through the concept of ordered pairs, and emphasis is placed on the logical basis for the routine operations performed. Since the point of view of the program is modern, the material should also be quite helpful to persons who have previously studied algebra and who would like to review, and, at the same time, modernize their point of view toward the subject.

The units in the program are sequential, and, with the exception of Unit I, there are certain prerequisites necessary for each. Every volume, except Volume I, includes a prerequisite test, together with a suggested minimum score. This score is to be viewed as flexible. The primary purpose of the test is to provide the individual student with a means of determining whether or not he can expect to complete the material in the volume without undue difficulty.

IRVING DROOYAN
WILLIAM WOOTON

HOW TO USE THIS MATERIAL

The theory underlying programmed instruction is quite simple. The program presents you with information in small units called frames, and, at the same time, requires you to make frequent and active written responses in the form of a word, a phrase, or a symbol. Programmed material is only as effective as you, the student, make it. In order to achieve the maximum benefit from this unit, you should follow the following instructions carefully.

If you wish to measure what you learn, you should take one form of the self-evaluation tests at the end of Unit I before beginning the program. Then, after completing the unit, you can take the alternate form of the test and compare the two scores. The same procedure can be used for Unit II.

To progress through the program:

1. Place the response shield over the response column (the column on the left-hand side of the page) so that the entire column is covered.

2. Read the first frame on the right-hand side of the page carefully, noting, as you do, the place where you are asked to respond. Do not write a response until you have read the entire frame.

3. After deciding on the proper response, write it in the blank provided or at the end of the frame.

4. Slide the response shield down until it is level with the top of the next frame. This will uncover the correct response to the preceding frame and any additional remarks accompanying it.

5. Verify that you have made the correct response. You should almost always have done so, because the frames were constructed in such fashion that it will be difficult for you to make an error.

6. If you have made the correct response, repeat Steps 2 to 5 above with the next frame. If you have made an error on the frame, read the frame again, draw a line through your incorrect response and write the correct response. Following this, repeat Steps 2 to 5 above.

Essentially, this is all there is to your part of the task, and the program must assume the remainder of the responsibility for your learning. However, there are a few additional things you can do to improve the effectiveness of the material.

1. Do not try to go too fast. Each frame should be read carefully and you should think about the response you are going to make. Does it fit the wording of the frame? Does it make sense? In many frames you will find clues (called prompts) that are designed to aid you in making a correct response. Does your proposed response match the clue?

2. Mathematics is a language written in symbols. In order to understand mathematics, you have to make a conscious effort to read the symbolism as though it were written out in words.

3. Do not try to do too much at once. If you stay with your work too long at one time, you tend to become impatient, and the number of errors you make will probably rise. If you are making good progress, and are not tired, there is no reason to stop, but if you find yourself becoming bored, or find yourself making a high percentage of errors, take a break. Come back to the program later.

4. After taking a break, pick up your work a few frames behind where you stopped work. This will lead you back into the logical sequence with a minimum of confusion.

5. Do not be overly attentive to the remarks that accompany some of the responses in the response column. They are there to clear up points of confusion once in a while, but if you are not confused, don't waste time on them. The important thing as far as you are concerned is the response itself.

6. Complete the unit. If you do not complete the unit, you cannot expect to achieve the full benefit of the material.

Upon completion of the unit, the student should:

1. Be able to apply the fundamental principle of fractions both in the form $\frac{ac}{bc} = \frac{a}{b}$ to reduce fractions to lower terms, and in the form $\frac{a}{b} = \frac{ac}{bc}$, to build fractions to higher terms.

2. Be able to perform routine arithmetical operations on fractions whose numerators or denominators or both are polynomial expressions (through trinomials).

3. Be able to solve simple first-degree equations in which the variables contain fractional coefficients.

4. Be able to solve simple fractional equations equivalent to first-degree equations.

5. Be able to solve simple word problems expressible in terms of first-degree equations or in terms of fractional equations equivalent to first-degree equations.

6. Know that ratios are fractions and that proportions are a special case of fractional equations, demonstrating this knowledge by being able to solve simple word problems expressible as proportions.

CONTENTS

	Topics begin on	
	Page	Frame
Definitions.	1	1
Fractions in higher terms	4	20
Fractions in lower terms	11	63
Changing signs associated with fractions.	22	139
Addition of fractions	31	199
Division of polynomials	63	433
Multiplication of fractions	74	488
Division of fractions	80	526
Complex fractions.	86	562
Equations containing fractions.	91	592
Proportion.	98	640
Word problems.	102	668
Review	113	724
Self-evaluation test, Form A.	120	
Self-evaluation test, Form B.	121	
Answers to tests.	122	

PREREQUISITE TEST

Complete this test and score your paper from the answers at the end of this unit.

Write as equal expressions without parentheses and in simplest form.

1. $2(a^2 + 4a) - 3(a + 5)$
2. $(a + 2)(a - 5)$
3. $(a + 4)^2$
4. $3(3a - 1)(2a + 1)$

Represent in completely factored form.

5. 24
6. $a^2 - a$
7. $x^2 - 8x + 16$
8. $x^2 - 16$
9. $2x^2 - 5x - 12$
10. $2x^2 - xy - y^2$
11. $9x^2 - 4y^2$

Solve for x

12. $6x - 3 = 8x + 7$
13. $\dfrac{3x}{4} - 6 = 0$
14. $4 - \dfrac{2}{3}x = 6$
15. $6(x - 1) + x = -13$

If you missed more than four items on this test, you are probably not adequately prepared to start Unit V. We suggest you prepare yourself by working through earlier units of Programmed Beginning Algebra.

Unit V

Fractions and Fractional Equations

Remark. In this unit you will learn how to work with algebraic fractions, and become acquainted with some of the principles upon which such work is based. We shall begin by reviewing some vocabulary associated with fractions.

fraction

1. The indicated quotient of two expressions is called a fraction. A fraction is, therefore, a symbol. $\frac{x+1}{3}$ is a fraction because it is the indicated quotient of the expressions $x+1$ and 3. $\frac{3}{5}$ is also a _____.

fraction

2. The symbol $\frac{x^2 + x + 1}{4}$ is a _____.

$x + 1$

3. A fraction consists of three parts, a bar, called a "fraction bar," and two expressions, one written above the fraction bar and one below. The expression above the fraction bar is called the numerator of the fraction. The numerator of the fraction $\frac{x+1}{3}$ is_____.

numerator

4. In the fraction $\frac{3x}{7}$, $3x$ is the_____.

ANSWERS

Prerequisite Test

1. $2a^2 + 5a - 15$ 　　　　 2. $a^2 - 3a - 10$ 　　　　 3. $a^2 + 8a + 16$

4. $18a^2 + 3a - 3$ 　　　　 5. $2 \cdot 2 \cdot 2 \cdot 3$ 　　　　 6. $a(a - 1)$

7. $(x - 4)(x - 4)$ 　　　　 8. $(x - 4)(x + 4)$ 　　　　 9. $(2x + 3)(x - 4)$

10. $(2x + y)(x - y)$ 　　 11. $(3x - 2y)(3x + 2y)$ 　 12. -5

13. 8 　　　　 14. -3 　　　　 15. -1

Form A

1. $\dfrac{2x}{y^2}$ 　　　　 2. $\dfrac{1}{a + 1}$ 　　　　 3. 2

4. $\dfrac{x}{4}$ 　　　　 5. $\dfrac{-1}{(a - 1)(a + 1)}$ 　　 6. $x + 6 + \dfrac{7}{x - 1}$

7. $\dfrac{4x^2}{y}$ 　　　　 8. 1 　　　　 9. $\dfrac{x - 1}{2x}$

10. $\dfrac{a - 2}{a + 3}$ 　　 11. $\dfrac{4a - 6}{4a + 1}$ 　　 12. 6

13. 3 　　　　 14. 3 　　　　 15. $\dfrac{36}{5}$ days

Form B

1. $\dfrac{3y^2}{x}$ 　　　　 2. $\dfrac{1}{a - 5}$ 　　　　 3. -4

4. $\dfrac{x - 3}{3}$ 　　　　 5. $\dfrac{1}{(a + 1)(a - 1)}$ 　　 6. $x - 5 + \dfrac{11}{x + 2}$

7. $\dfrac{9xy}{2}$ 　　　　 8. 1 　　　　 9. $\dfrac{3(x + 1)}{x}$

10. $\dfrac{a + 2}{a - 4}$ 　　 11. $\dfrac{4a + 2}{4a - 3}$ 　　 12. $-\dfrac{4}{3}$

13. 4 　　　　 14. -1 　　　　 15. $24;\ 9$

5

5. The expression below the fraction bar in a fraction is called the denominator of the fraction. The denominator of the fraction $\frac{7}{5}$ is_____.

denominator

6. In the fraction $\frac{x^2 + 1}{7}$, 7 is the_____.

numerator; denominator

7. In the fraction $\frac{4}{9}$, 4 is the_____ and 9 is the_____.

$\frac{6}{1}$

8. The number twelve can be represented by the fraction $\frac{12}{1}$ and the number six by the fraction_____.

meaningless

9. Since a fraction is an indicated quotient and because division by 0 is meaningless, any fraction whose denominator is 0 is meaningless. Thus, $\frac{7}{0}$ does not represent a number and is meaningless. $\frac{3}{0}$ is _____.

undefined

"meaningless" will do.

10. In mathematical language, the word "undefined" is often used instead of "meaningless." The expression $\frac{8}{0}$ does not represent a number and is, therefore, _____.

undefined

11. The fraction $\frac{13}{0}$ is_____.

SELF-EVALUATION TEST, FORM B

1. Reduce $\dfrac{12xy^3}{4x^2y}$ to lowest terms.

2. Reduce $\dfrac{a+1}{a^2-4a-5}$ to lowest terms.

3. The symbol $\dfrac{3x}{4+x}$ is undefined if x equals_____.

4. Write $\dfrac{x-2}{3} - \dfrac{1}{3}$ as a single fraction.

5. Write $\dfrac{a}{a^2-1} - \dfrac{1}{a+1}$ as a single fraction.

6. $(x^2 - 3x + 1) \div (x + 2) =$ _____.

7. Simplify $\dfrac{3x^2}{4y} \cdot \dfrac{6y^2}{x}$.

8. $\dfrac{x^2+7x+6}{x^2-1} \cdot \dfrac{x-1}{x+6} =$ _____.

9. $\dfrac{x^2-1}{3} \div \dfrac{x^2-x}{9} =$ _____.

10. Simplify $\dfrac{1+\dfrac{2}{a}}{1-\dfrac{4}{a}}$.

11. Simplify $\dfrac{a+\dfrac{1}{2}}{a-\dfrac{3}{4}}$.

12. Solve $\dfrac{2x}{3} + \dfrac{4}{9} = \dfrac{x}{3}$.

13. Solve $\dfrac{y}{2+y} = \dfrac{2}{3}$.

14. Solve $\dfrac{14}{x-1} + \dfrac{1}{x} = \dfrac{8}{x}$.

15. The width of a rectangle is $\dfrac{3}{8}$ of the length. If the perimeter is 66 feet, the length is_____feet and the width is_____feet.

0

12. If x represents an integer, $\dfrac{3}{x}$ represents a number for all values of x except 0. If y represents an integer, $\dfrac{7}{y}$ represents a number for all values of y except_____.

0

13. If x represents an integer, $\dfrac{2}{x-1}$ represents a number for all values of x except 1, because if x is replaced by 1, the denominator has the value_____.

0

14. A fraction whose numerator is 0 and whose denominator is not 0 has a value of 0. Thus, $\dfrac{0}{4} = 0$ and $\dfrac{0}{7} = 0$. $\dfrac{0}{3} =$_____.

0; undefined

"meaningless" is also correct.

15. $\dfrac{0}{5}$ equals_____ and $\dfrac{5}{0}$ is_____.

0

16. A fraction whose numerator and denominator are both 0 is undefined. Thus, $\dfrac{0}{0}$ is undefined, and $\dfrac{x}{x}$ is undefined if x has the value 0. $\dfrac{y}{y}$ is undefined if y has the value_____.

0

17. The fractions $\dfrac{12}{0}$ and $\dfrac{0}{0}$ are undefined but the fraction $\dfrac{0}{12}$ equals_____.

SELF-EVALUATION TEST, FORM A

1. Reduce $\dfrac{6x^2y}{3xy^3}$ to lowest terms.

2. Reduce $\dfrac{a-3}{a^2-2a-3}$ to lowest terms.

3. The symbol $\dfrac{3x}{x-2}$ is undefined if x equals _____.

4. Write $\dfrac{x+3}{4} - \dfrac{3}{4}$ as a single fraction.

5. Write $\dfrac{a}{a^2-1} - \dfrac{1}{a-1}$ as a single fraction.

6. $(x^2 + 5x + 1) \div (x - 1) = $ _____ .

7. Simplify $\dfrac{2xy}{3} \cdot \dfrac{6x}{y^2}$.

8. $\dfrac{x^2-7x+6}{x^2-1} \cdot \dfrac{x+1}{x-6} = $ _____ .

9. $\dfrac{x^2-1}{4} \div \dfrac{x^2+x}{2} = $ _____ .

10. Simplify $\dfrac{1-\dfrac{2}{a}}{1+\dfrac{3}{a}}$.

11. Simplify $\dfrac{a-\dfrac{3}{2}}{a+\dfrac{1}{4}}$.

12. Solve $\dfrac{x}{2} + 1 = \dfrac{2x}{3}$.

13. Solve $\dfrac{6}{x} = \dfrac{16}{x+5}$.

14. Solve $1 - \dfrac{3+y}{2y} = \dfrac{3-y}{y}$.

15. If a man can do a job in twelve days and another man can do the job in eighteen days, how many days would be required for them to complete the job while working together?

0

$\frac{0}{0-1} = \frac{0}{1} = 0.$

18. $\frac{x}{x-1}$ is undefined when x has the value 1, but when x is equal to 0, the fraction $\frac{x}{x-1}$ has the value

____.

0

19. When y has the value -2, $\frac{y+2}{y}$ equals____.

Remark. What all of this adds up to is that if the numerator of a fraction is 0, and the denominator is not 0, then the fraction represents 0. However, if the denominator of a fraction is 0, regardless of the value of the numerator, the fraction is undefined. Let us make an agreement now, that any variables in the denominators of the fractions with which we will be working in this unit will not take on values that will cause the denominator to become zero.

We shall next turn our attention to what is meant by equal fractions, and how fractions in one form are transformed to equal fractions in another form. To do this we shall first need to discuss the multiplication of two fractions.

$\frac{10}{27}$

Or $\frac{2 \cdot 5}{3 \cdot 9}$.

20. The product of two fractions $\frac{a}{b}$ and $\frac{c}{d}$ is defined to be the fraction $\frac{ac}{bd}$. Thus $\frac{3}{2} \cdot \frac{5}{7} = \frac{3 \cdot 5}{2 \cdot 7} = \frac{15}{14}$. Similarly, $\frac{2}{3} \cdot \frac{5}{9} =$ _____.

$\frac{2}{15}$

Or $\frac{2 \cdot 1}{3 \cdot 5}$.

21. The product of $\frac{2}{3}$ and $\frac{1}{5}$ equals _____.

$\frac{20}{21}$

22. $\frac{4}{7} \cdot \frac{5}{3} =$ _____.

proportion

757. Any equation of the form $\frac{a}{b} = \frac{c}{d}$ that relates two ratios, is called a _____ .

bd

758. $\frac{a}{b} = \frac{c}{d}$ can be transformed to the equivalent equation $ad = bc$ by multiplying each member by _____, the LCD of the fractions.

extremes; means

759. In a proportion $\frac{a}{b} = \frac{c}{d}$, a and d are called the extremes and b and c are called the means. Since $ad = bc$, the product of the _____ equals the product of the _____ .

-2

760. Solve $\frac{2}{3} = \frac{x-2}{x-4}$.

Remark. This concludes Unit V. To see what you have learned, you can take one of the self-evaluation tests that follow. If you completed one form before starting this unit, we suggest that you use the alternate form now.

$\dfrac{4}{5}$

23. Any number times 1 equals itself. Thus,

$3 \cdot 1 = 3$ and $\dfrac{4}{5} \cdot 1 = \underline{\hphantom{xxxx}}$.

$\dfrac{a}{b}$

24. $\dfrac{a}{b} \cdot 1 = \underline{\hphantom{xxxx}}$.

1

25. Since any number divided by itself is 1, the fraction $\dfrac{c}{c}$ is equal to 1. The fraction $\dfrac{a}{a}$ is equal to $\underline{\hphantom{xxxx}}$.

1

26. $\dfrac{2}{2} = \dfrac{3}{3} = \dfrac{4}{4} = 1$. $\dfrac{5}{5} = \underline{\hphantom{xxxx}}$.

1

27. $\dfrac{6}{6} = \underline{\hphantom{xxxx}}$.

$\dfrac{1}{2}$

28. If the fraction $\dfrac{1}{2}$ is multiplied by $\dfrac{6}{6}$, the result is $\dfrac{1}{2} \cdot \dfrac{6}{6} = \dfrac{6}{12}$. Since $\dfrac{1}{2}$ has been multiplied by 1 $\left(\dfrac{6}{6} \text{ is equal to } 1 \right)$, the result, $\dfrac{6}{12}$, is equal to $\underline{\hphantom{xxxx}}$.

$\dfrac{2}{3} = \dfrac{4}{6}$

29. If the fraction $\dfrac{2}{3}$ is multiplied by $\dfrac{2}{2}$, the result is $\dfrac{2}{3} \cdot \dfrac{2}{2} = \dfrac{4}{6}$. Since $\dfrac{2}{3}$ has been multiplied by 1 $\left(\dfrac{2}{2} \text{ is equal} \right.$ to $\left. 1 \right)$, the result, $\dfrac{4}{6}$, is equal to $\dfrac{2}{3}$. That is,

$\dfrac{2}{3} = \underline{\hphantom{xxxxxxx}}$.

$\dfrac{2x}{x-1}$

You first have
$\dfrac{x(x+1)}{3} \cdot \dfrac{6}{(x-1)(x+1)}$.

752. Write the quotient $\dfrac{x^2 + x}{3} \div \dfrac{x^2 - 1}{6}$ as a a single fraction in lowest terms.

complex fraction

753. Any fraction that contains one or more fractions in its numerator or denominator is called a complex fraction. $\dfrac{\frac{2}{3}}{\frac{x}{7}}$ is a _____

_____ .

$\dfrac{2}{3}$

754. $\dfrac{\frac{x-1}{5}}{\frac{3x-3}{10}}$ can be written as $\dfrac{x-1}{5} \div \dfrac{3x-3}{10}$ or as

$\dfrac{x-1}{5} \cdot \dfrac{10}{3(x-1)}$. If the numerator and denominator are divided by their common factors, the result

is _____ .

$\dfrac{3b-a}{4a-2b}$

You first have
$\dfrac{\left(\frac{3}{a} - \frac{1}{b}\right)ab}{\left(\frac{4}{b} - \frac{2}{a}\right)ab}$

755. $\dfrac{\frac{3}{a} - \frac{1}{b}}{\frac{4}{b} - \frac{2}{a}}$, when written as a simple fraction,

appears as _____ .

12; 24

756. Equations that have identical solutions are called equivalent equations. $\dfrac{3x}{4} - \dfrac{2x}{3} = 2$ can be transformed to the equivalent equations $9x - 8x = 24$ that does not contain fractions by multiplying each member by_____ , the LCD of the fractions. The solution of the original equation is_____ .

$\frac{21}{24}$

30. $\frac{3}{4} \cdot \frac{4}{4} = \frac{12}{16}$. Since $\frac{4}{4}$ is 1, $\frac{3}{4} = \frac{12}{16}$. Similarly,

$\frac{7}{8} \cdot \frac{3}{3} = \frac{21}{24}$. Therefore, $\frac{7}{8}$ equals _____.

$\frac{1}{2} = \frac{2}{4}$

Or $\frac{1}{2}$ equals $\frac{2}{4}$.

31. $\left(\frac{1}{2}\right)\left(\frac{2}{2}\right) = \frac{2}{4}$, therefore, $\underline{\frac{1}{2}} \quad \underline{\frac{2}{4}}$.

equal

32. $\left(\frac{x^2}{2}\right)\left(\frac{3x}{3x}\right) = \frac{3x^3}{6x}$, therefore, $\frac{x^2}{2}$ and $\frac{3x^3}{6x}$ are

_____.

terms

33. The numerator and denominator of a fraction are frequently referred to as the terms of the fraction. Thus, 3 and 5 are the _____ of the fraction $\frac{3}{5}$.

higher

34. $\frac{2}{3} = \frac{4}{6}$. The fraction $\frac{4}{6}$ is said to be in higher

terms than the equal fraction $\frac{2}{3}$, because $\frac{4}{6}$ can be ob-

tained from $\frac{2}{3}$ by multiplying by $\frac{2}{2}$. That is, $\frac{2}{3} \cdot \frac{2}{2} = \frac{4}{6}$.

Because $\frac{3}{4} \cdot \frac{3}{3} = \frac{9}{12}$, $\frac{9}{12}$ is in _____ terms than

$\frac{3}{4}$.

higher terms

35. Since $\frac{5}{7} \cdot \frac{3}{3} = \frac{15}{21}$, $\frac{15}{21}$ is in _____

_____ than $\frac{5}{7}$.

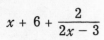

$x + 6 + \dfrac{2}{2x - 3}$

746. Write the results in the preceding frame as the sum of a polynomial expression and a fraction.

$\dfrac{1}{10}$

Or $\dfrac{1}{5 \cdot 2}$.

747. The product of two fractions such as $\dfrac{2}{15} \cdot \dfrac{3}{4}$ can be simplified by first writing $\dfrac{2}{3 \cdot 5} \cdot \dfrac{3}{2 \cdot 2}$, and then $\dfrac{1}{5 \cdot 2} \left(\dfrac{2 \cdot 3}{2 \cdot 3} \right)$. Upon the application of the fundamental principle this latter expression becomes _____.

$\dfrac{1}{10}$

748. The slant bar can be used to indicate the division of common factors from numerators and denominators. Thus, $\dfrac{\cancel{2}}{\cancel{15}} \cdot \dfrac{\cancel{3}}{\cancel{4}} = \dfrac{1 \cdot 1}{5 \cdot 2} = $ _____ .

$x - 1$

You first have
$\dfrac{\cancel{(x+5)}\cancel{(x+1)}}{\cancel{(x-1)}\cancel{(x+1)}} \cdot \dfrac{\cancel{(x-1)}(x-1)}{\cancel{(x+5)}}$.

749. $\dfrac{x^2 + 6x + 5}{x^2 - 1} \cdot \dfrac{x^2 - 2x + 1}{x + 5}$ can be simplified and written as _____ .

$\left(\dfrac{1}{4} \right) \left(\dfrac{5}{2} \right)$

750. Since the quotient $\dfrac{a}{b} \div \dfrac{c}{d}$ can be written as the equal product $\dfrac{a}{b} \cdot \dfrac{d}{c}$, $\dfrac{1}{4} \div \dfrac{2}{5}$ can be written as $\left(\dfrac{1}{4} \right) \left(\right)$.

$\left(\dfrac{x-1}{2} \right) \left(\dfrac{4}{3x} \right)$

751. $\dfrac{x - 1}{2} \div \dfrac{3x}{4}$ can be written as the equal product $\left(\right) \left(\right)$.

fundamental

36. The terms of a fraction can be changed by applying what is called the fundamental principle of fractions. In symbols, the fundamental principle is given by

$$\frac{a}{b} = \frac{ac}{bc}.$$

Thus, changing $\frac{2}{3}$ to the equal fraction $\frac{4}{6}$ by multiplying by $\frac{2}{2}$ is an application of the _____ principle of fractions.

$\frac{2}{2}$

37. $\frac{3}{5}$ is changed to the equal fraction $\frac{6}{10}$ by multiplying by _____ .

$\frac{4}{4}$; higher

38. $\frac{4}{5}$ is changed to the equal fraction $\frac{16}{20}$ by multiplying by _____ . $\frac{16}{20}$ is in _____ terms than $\frac{4}{5}$.

$\frac{3}{3}$

39. $\frac{3}{5}$ can be changed to the equal fraction $\frac{9}{15}$ by multiplying $\frac{3}{5}$ by _____ .

$\frac{4a}{4b}$

40. $\frac{a}{b} = \frac{a}{b}\left(\frac{4}{4}\right) = $ _____ .

$\frac{a4}{b4}$ is correct, but we generally write numerals ahead of variables in a product.

$\frac{12a}{18b}$

41. $\frac{2a}{3b} = \frac{2a}{3b}\left(\frac{6}{6}\right) = $ _____ .

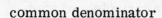

common denominator

24

$\dfrac{7}{8}$

You first have $\dfrac{21}{24}$.

$2(x + 1)(x - 2)$

$\dfrac{7x^2 - 2x}{2(x + 1)(x - 2)}$

$x - 7$

$x + 6;\ \ 2$

739. To add fractions that do not have a common denominator, it is necessary to change one or both fractions to equal fractions that have a _____ _____.

740. The least common denominator of $\dfrac{1}{3}$, $\dfrac{5}{6}$, and $\dfrac{3}{8}$ is _____.

741. $\dfrac{1}{3} + \dfrac{1}{6} + \dfrac{3}{8} = \dfrac{1(8)}{3(8)} + \dfrac{1(4)}{6(4)} + \dfrac{3(3)}{8(3)}$ and this latter expression can be combined as a single fraction which, when reduced to lowest terms, is _____.

742. The least common denominator of $\dfrac{3x}{2x + 2}$ and $\dfrac{4x}{2x - 4}$ is _____.

743. $\dfrac{3x}{2x + 2} + \dfrac{4x}{2x - 4} = \dfrac{3x}{2(x - 1)}\dfrac{(x - 2)}{(x - 2)} + \dfrac{4x}{2(x - 2)}\dfrac{(x + 1)}{(x + 1)}$ and this latter expression can be combined as a single fraction which, when simplified, appears as _____.

744. To divide $x^2 - 5x - 14$ by $x + 2$, the expressions are arranged $x + 2\,)\overline{x^2 - 5x - 14}$, and then the division is accomplished in the same manner as the long division of arithmetic. The quotient when $x^2 - 5x - 14$ is divided by $x + 2$ is_____.

745. Divide $2x^2 + 9x - 16$ by $2x - 3$. The quotient is_____ and the remainder is_____.

$\dfrac{3x^2y}{3z}$

42. $\dfrac{x^2y}{z} = \dfrac{x^2y}{z}\left(\dfrac{3}{3}\right) = $ _____ .

$\dfrac{2x^2y}{3y}$

43. $\dfrac{2x^2}{3} = \dfrac{2x^2}{3}\left(\dfrac{y}{y}\right) = $ _____ .

$\dfrac{12}{4}$

44. $3 = 3\left(\dfrac{4}{4}\right) = \dfrac{3}{1}\left(\dfrac{4}{4}\right) = $ _____ .

$\dfrac{3a}{3}$

45. $a = a\left(\dfrac{3}{3}\right) = \dfrac{a}{1}\left(\dfrac{3}{3}\right) = $ _____ .

$\dfrac{xy^3}{y^2}$

46. $xy = xy\left(\dfrac{y^2}{y^2}\right) = $ _____ .

Remark. Is it clear that if you want to change a fraction to higher terms, you just multiply the numerator and denominator by the same number? (Of course, you cannot use 0 as a multiplier.) In fact, we shall give a name to the number used to multiply the numerator and denominator.

building

47. The number by which both numerator and denominator are multiplied in building a fraction to an equal fraction in higher terms is called the building factor. Thus, to change $\dfrac{3}{7}$ to $\dfrac{9}{21}$, the numerator and denominator of $\dfrac{3}{7}$ are multiplied by the _____ factor, 3.

6

48. To obtain a building factor that will change $\dfrac{3}{4}$ to an equal fraction, $\dfrac{?}{24}$, you ask "By what number must 4 be multiplied to yield 24?" Since the answer is 6, the desired building factor is____.

$\dfrac{5}{12}$

$\dfrac{-5}{12}$

distributive law

$\dfrac{5x}{9y}$

$\dfrac{3}{x-y}$

734. A fraction with a positive sign on the denominator and a positive sign on the fraction such as $\dfrac{-a}{b}$ or $\dfrac{a}{b}$ is generally the most convenient form to use, and such fractions are said to be in standard form. $\dfrac{-5}{-12}$, $-\dfrac{5}{-12}$, and $-\dfrac{-5}{12}$ can all be written in the standard form _____ .

735. $\dfrac{5}{-12}$, $-\dfrac{5}{12}$, and $-\dfrac{-5}{-12}$ can all be written in standard form as _____ .

736. $\dfrac{a}{c} + \dfrac{b}{c}$ can be written as $a\left(\dfrac{1}{c}\right) + b\left(\dfrac{1}{c}\right)$. The fact that the sum of two fractions $a\left(\dfrac{1}{c}\right) + b\left(\dfrac{1}{c}\right)$ can be written as the single fraction $(a+b)\dfrac{1}{c}$ or $\dfrac{a+b}{c}$ is guaranteed by the distributive law. Writing $\dfrac{3}{11} + \dfrac{5}{11}$ as $\dfrac{8}{11}$ is an application of the _____ .

737. Since $\dfrac{a}{c} + \dfrac{b}{c} = \dfrac{a+b}{c}$, except if c equals 0, the sum of any two fractions having the same nonzero denominator can be written as a single fraction with a numerator equal to the sum of the two numerators and having the common denominator of the fractions. Thus, $\dfrac{x}{9y} + \dfrac{4x}{9y} =$ _____ .

738. $\dfrac{8}{x-y} - \dfrac{5}{x-y} =$ _____ .

$\dfrac{18}{24}$

49. $\dfrac{3}{4} = \dfrac{3}{4}\left(\dfrac{6}{6}\right) = $ _____ .

4

50. 7 must be multiplied by 4 to yield 28. Therefore, the building factor necessary to change $\dfrac{3}{7}$ to an equal fraction $\dfrac{?}{28}$ is _____ .

$\dfrac{12}{28}$

51. $\dfrac{3}{7} = \dfrac{3}{7}\left(\dfrac{4}{4}\right) = $ _____ .

$\dfrac{5}{5}$

52. $\dfrac{x}{y}\left(\rule{2cm}{0.4pt}\right) = \dfrac{5x}{5y}$.

$\dfrac{x}{x}$

53. $\dfrac{x^2}{y}\left(\rule{2cm}{0.4pt}\right) = \dfrac{x^3}{xy}$.

$\dfrac{3yz}{3yz}$

54. $\dfrac{x^2 y}{z}\left(\rule{2.5cm}{0.4pt}\right) = \dfrac{3x^2 y^2 z}{3yz^2}$.

$\dfrac{3y}{3y}$

55. $x^2\left(\rule{2.5cm}{0.4pt}\right) = \dfrac{3x^2 y}{3y}$.

Remark. The numerators and denominators of the fractions you have been studying have consisted of monomials. The process used to change a fraction to an equal fraction in higher terms is also applicable to fractions whose numerators or denominators contain more than one term.

$\dfrac{2}{3}$

730. The symbolic form $\dfrac{ac}{bc} = \dfrac{a}{b}$ where b and c do not equal zero is an alternative form of the fundamental principle of fractions and justifies reducing $\dfrac{2x}{3x}$ to _____ .

lowest

731. $\dfrac{2x}{3x}$ and $\dfrac{2}{3}$ are equal for all values of x except 0. $\dfrac{2}{3}$ is in _____ terms, while $\dfrac{2x}{3x}$ is not.

$\dfrac{12}{18}$; $\dfrac{2}{3}$

732. Various forms can be used to show the reduction of fractions to lower terms. Thus,

$$\dfrac{12}{18} = \dfrac{2 \cdot 6}{3 \cdot 6} = \dfrac{2}{3}\left(\dfrac{6}{6}\right) = \dfrac{2}{3}(1) = \dfrac{2}{3},$$

$$\dfrac{12}{18} = \dfrac{2 \cdot 6}{3 \cdot 6} = \dfrac{2}{3},$$

$$\dfrac{12}{18} = \dfrac{12 \div 6}{18 \div 6} = \dfrac{2}{3}, \text{ and}$$

$$\dfrac{\overset{2}{\cancel{12}}}{\underset{3}{\cancel{18}}} = \dfrac{2}{3}$$

represent the reduction of the fraction _____ to the

fraction _____ .

two

733. A fraction can be changed to an equal fraction by changing any two of the three signs associated with a fraction. When $\dfrac{-2}{-3}$ is written as the equal fraction $\dfrac{2}{3}$, _____ signs have been changed.

$$\frac{3x - 6}{5x - 10}$$

56. $\frac{2}{3} = \frac{2}{3}\left(\frac{x + 3}{x + 3}\right) = \frac{2(x + 3)}{3(x + 3)} = \frac{2x + 6}{3x + 9}$.

Similarly, $\frac{3}{5}\left(\frac{x - 2}{x - 2}\right) = \frac{3(x - 2)}{5(x - 2)} = $ _____ .

$$\frac{4a^2 + 24a}{5a + 30}$$

57. $\frac{4a}{5} = \frac{4a}{5}\left(\frac{a + 6}{a + 6}\right) = \frac{4a(a + 6)}{5(a + 6)} = $ _____ .

$$\frac{3x^2 - 3x}{x - 1}$$

58. $3x = 3x\left(\frac{x - 1}{x - 1}\right) = \frac{3x(x - 1)}{1\,(x - 1)} = $ _____ .

$$\frac{a^2 - ab}{ab - b^2}$$

59. $\frac{a}{b} = \frac{a}{b}\left(\frac{a - b}{a - b}\right) = \frac{a(a - b)}{b(a - b)} = $ _____ .

$$\frac{x^2 - 2x + 1}{x^2 - x}$$

60. $\frac{x - 1}{x} = \frac{(x - 1)}{x}\left(\frac{x - 1}{x - 1}\right) = \frac{(x - 1)(x - 1)}{x(x - 1)} = $

_____ .

$$\frac{4a^2 - 1}{2a^2 + a}$$

61. $\frac{2a - 1}{a} = \frac{(2a - 1)}{a}\left(\frac{2a + 1}{2a + 1}\right) = $ _____ .

$$\frac{a^2 - b^2}{a^2 + 2ab + b^2}$$

62. $\frac{a - b}{a + b} = \frac{(a - b)}{(a + b)}\left(\frac{a + b}{a + b}\right) = $ _____ .

Remark. The fundamental principle of fractions can be used not only to transform a fraction to an equal fraction in higher terms, but, if the fundamental principle is written $\frac{ac}{bc} = \frac{a}{b}$ instead of $\frac{a}{b} = \frac{ac}{bc}$, it can also be invoked to write certain fractions in lower terms.

fraction

724. The indicated quotient of two expressions such as $\dfrac{x-4}{3}$ is called a_____.

7

725. Since division by zero is undefined the fraction $\dfrac{8}{x}$ is not defined for a value of x equal to 0. The fraction $\dfrac{5}{x-7}$ is not defined for a value of x equal to_____.

are

726. Any number times 1 equals itself. Thus, $\dfrac{2}{3}(1) = \dfrac{2}{3}$. Since $\dfrac{4}{4}$ equals 1, $\dfrac{2}{3}\left(\dfrac{4}{4}\right)$ or $\dfrac{8}{12}$ and $\dfrac{2}{3}$ (are/are not) equal fractions.

are

727. $\dfrac{a}{b}(1) = \dfrac{a}{b}$. Since $\dfrac{c}{c}$ equals 1 for all values of c except 0, $\dfrac{a}{b}\left(\dfrac{c}{c}\right)$ or $\dfrac{ac}{bc}$ and $\dfrac{a}{b}$ (are/are not) equal fractions.

fundamental principle

728. The fact that $\dfrac{a}{b} = \dfrac{ac}{bc}$ for all values of a, b, and c, except that b and c cannot equal 0, is called the fundamental principle of fractions. Writing $\dfrac{3}{4} = \dfrac{6}{8}$ is an application of the_____ _____ of fractions.

is not

729. If the numerator and denominator of a fraction contain no common factor, then the fraction is said to be in lowest terms. $\dfrac{6}{8}$ (is/is not) in lowest terms.

$\dfrac{c}{c}$

63. $\dfrac{ac}{bc}$ is in higher terms than $\dfrac{a}{b}$ because $\dfrac{ac}{bc}$ can be obtained from $\dfrac{a}{b}$ by multiplying by $\left(\underline{\qquad}\right)$.

lower

64. Since $\dfrac{ac}{bc}$ is in higher terms than $\dfrac{a}{b}$, $\dfrac{a}{b}$ is said to be in lower terms than $\dfrac{ac}{bc}$. Thus, $\dfrac{1}{2}$ is in lower terms than $\dfrac{2}{4}$ and $\dfrac{1}{3}$ is in _____ terms than $\dfrac{2}{6}$.

lower terms

65. Recall that $\dfrac{a}{b} = \dfrac{ac}{bc}$ is called the fundamental principle of fractions. $\dfrac{ac}{bc} = \dfrac{a}{b}$ is an alternative form in which the right member $\dfrac{a}{b}$ is in _____ _____ than $\dfrac{ac}{bc}$.

$\dfrac{5}{8}$

66. The fraction $\dfrac{10}{16}$ can be "reduced" to an equal fraction in lower terms by writing the numerator and denominator in factored form, $\dfrac{5 \cdot 2}{8 \cdot 2}$ or $\left(\dfrac{5}{8}\right)\left(\dfrac{2}{2}\right)$; and, since $\dfrac{2}{2} = 1$, $\left(\dfrac{5}{8}\right)\left(\dfrac{2}{2}\right) = \dfrac{5}{8}(1) = \underline{\qquad}$.

$\dfrac{1}{2}$

67. $\dfrac{3}{6} = \dfrac{1 \cdot 3}{2 \cdot 3} = \dfrac{1}{2}\left(\dfrac{3}{3}\right) = \dfrac{1}{2}(1) = \underline{\qquad}$.

$\dfrac{2}{3}$

68. $\dfrac{8}{12} = \dfrac{2 \cdot 4}{3 \cdot 4} = \dfrac{2}{3}\left(\dfrac{4}{4}\right) = \dfrac{2}{3}(1) = \underline{\qquad}$.

40

720. The amount of coffee necessary to make the 3000 cups of coffee in Frame 718 is _____ pounds.

Remark. The key idea in working problems of this sort is that of a rate. A ratio can be viewed as a rate. Therefore, in setting up the proportions to solve problems like this, you should think of a rate of some kind. The rate might be miles per gallon, cups per pound, or, as in the next example, bricks per foot.

825

You first have $\frac{660}{24} = \frac{x}{30}$, where x represents the number of bricks required for 30 linear feet of wall.

721. If 660 bricks are required for 24 linear feet of wall, _____ bricks will be required for 30 linear feet.

$4.40

You first have $\frac{320}{80} = \frac{x}{110}$, where each ratio gives cents per pound.

722. If 80 pounds of nitrate costs $3.20, what would be the cost of 110 pounds?

$10\frac{1}{2}$ hours

You first have $\frac{40}{1} = \frac{420}{x}$.

723. Assuming a student works at a constant speed, if he completes 40 frames of a program in an hour, how long will it take him to complete a 420-frame program?

Remark. The remainder of this unit is a review. The last sequence of frames will give you an opportunity to obtain an overview of the unit in a very short time. Although you should not anticipate learning anything you have not learned to this point, the review will highlight the main ideas in a brief way and will reinforce what you have learned. If you feel the need of a review of the word problems just covered, it might be well to simply reread Frames 668 to 723.

● ●

lowest terms

69. A fraction with integers for numerator and denominator is said to be in <u>lowest terms</u> when the numerator and denominator contain no integral factors in common other than 1. Thus, $\frac{2}{3}$ is in _____ _____ because 2 and 3 contain no integral factor in common other than 1.

lowest terms

70. Because both 12 and 18 contain the common factor 6, $\frac{12}{18}$ is not in _____ _____ .

$\frac{2}{3}$

71. If $\frac{12}{18}$ is reduced by writing $\frac{12}{18} = \frac{2 \cdot 6}{3 \cdot 6} = \frac{2}{3}\left(\frac{6}{6}\right) = \left(\frac{2}{3}\right)(1) = \frac{2}{3}$, then $\frac{12}{18}$ has been reduced to _____ , which is in lowest terms.

5

72. $\frac{5}{30}$ is not in lowest terms because both the numerator and denominator contain the common factor _____ .

$\frac{1}{6}$

73. $\frac{5}{30}$ can be reduced to an equal fraction in lowest terms as follows: $\frac{5}{30} = \frac{1 \cdot 5}{6 \cdot 5} = \frac{1}{6}\left(\frac{5}{5}\right) = $ _____ .

lowest terms

74. Since 1 and 6 contain no common integral factors other than 1, $\frac{1}{6}$ is in _____ _____ .

$\frac{2}{3}$

75. When $\frac{14}{21}$ is reduced to an equal fraction in lowest terms, the result is _____ .

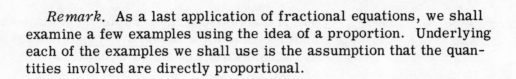

Remark. As a last application of fractional equations, we shall examine a few examples using the idea of a proportion. Underlying each of the examples we shall use is the assumption that the quantities involved are directly proportional.

30

$\frac{60}{2} = \frac{30}{1}$; $\frac{180}{6} = \frac{30}{1}$.

714. If it takes two hours to address sixty envelopes, then, at the same rate of addressing, it would take six hours to address 180 envelopes, because $\frac{60}{2} = \frac{180}{6}$. By reducing either of these fractions to lowest terms, it can be seen that the envelopes are addressed at the rate of _____ per hour.

$\frac{42}{3} = \frac{x}{5}$

715. If a car travels 42 miles on 3 gallons of gasoline, how far will it travel on 5 gallons? Assuming the rate of consumption to be constant, then 42 miles would be to 3 gallons as x miles is to 5 gallons. This leads to the equation _____.

70

716. The solution of $\frac{42}{3} = \frac{x}{5}$ is _____.

70

717. The car described in Frame 715 would, therefore, travel _____ miles on 5 gallons of gasoline.

$\frac{225}{3} = \frac{3000}{x}$

718. If 3 pounds of ground coffee will make 225 cups, how many pounds of coffee will be required to make 3000 cups? The equation used to describe this situation is _____.

40

719. The solution of $\frac{225}{3} = \frac{3000}{x}$ is _____.

$\dfrac{1}{3}$

76. Reduce $\dfrac{11}{33}$ to lowest terms.

$\dfrac{3}{5}$

77. Reduce $\dfrac{24}{40}$ to lowest terms.

Remark. Thus far we have reduced fractions such as $\dfrac{18}{38}$ to lowest terms by writing

$$\frac{18}{38} = \frac{9 \cdot 2}{19 \cdot 2} = \frac{9}{19}\left(\frac{2}{2}\right) = \frac{9}{19}(1) = \frac{9}{19}.$$

This process can be somewhat shortened by looking at the fundamental principle of fractions in a slightly different way.

$\dfrac{3}{4}$

78. The fundamental principle of fractions in the form

$$\frac{ac}{bc} = \frac{a}{b}$$

can be interpreted as follows:

If the numerator and denominator of a given fraction are each divided by the same non-zero number, the result is a fraction equal to the given fraction.

Thus, $\dfrac{4}{6} = \dfrac{4 \div 2}{6 \div 2} = \dfrac{2}{3}$ and $\dfrac{9}{12} = \dfrac{9 \div 3}{12 \div 3} = \underline{\quad}$.

$\dfrac{8}{13}$

79. $\dfrac{16}{26} = \dfrac{16 \div 2}{26 \div 2} = \underline{\quad}$.

$\dfrac{5}{7}$

80. $\dfrac{25}{35} = \dfrac{25 \div 5}{35 \div 5} = \underline{\quad}$.

$\frac{1}{4} + \frac{1}{6}$

709. If a man can do a job in six days and another man can do the same job in four days, then in one day, working together, they can do $\left(\underline{\quad + \quad} \right)$ part of the job.

$\frac{1}{x} = \frac{1}{4} + \frac{1}{6}$

710. Since $\frac{1}{x}$ represents the part of the job two men can do in one day, where x is the number of days required for the whole job, and since $\left(\frac{1}{4} + \frac{1}{6} \right)$ also represents the part of the job the men can do in one day, then $\frac{1}{x} = \underline{\qquad\qquad}$.

$\frac{12}{5}$

711. The solution of $\frac{1}{x} = \frac{1}{4} + \frac{1}{6}$ is $\underline{\qquad}$.

$\frac{12}{5}$

712. Since $\frac{12}{5}$ is the solution of $\frac{1}{x} = \frac{1}{4} + \frac{1}{6}$, the number of days required for both men working together to complete the job as described in Frame 710 is $\underline{\qquad}$.

$\frac{36}{7}$

You first have
$\frac{1}{x} = \frac{1}{9} + \frac{1}{12}$, where x represents the number of days to complete the job when both men work together.

713. If a man can do a job in twelve days and another man can do the job in nine days, it would require $\underline{\qquad}$ days for them to complete the job while working together.

divided

81. At times it is convenient to represent the division by common factors in the numerator and denominator by the use of a slant bar, $/$. Thus,

$$\frac{4}{6} = \frac{\overset{2}{\cancel{4}}}{\underset{3}{\cancel{6}}} = \frac{2}{3},$$

where the slant bar is used to indicate that 4 and 6 have each been _____ by the common factor 2.

2

82. $\frac{24}{26} = \frac{\overset{12}{\cancel{24}}}{\underset{13}{\cancel{26}}} = \frac{12}{13}$, where the slant bars indicate that 24 and 26 have each been divided by____.

$\frac{6}{7}$

83. $\frac{18}{21} = \frac{\overset{6}{\cancel{18}}}{\underset{7}{\cancel{21}}} =$ ____ .

13

84. $\frac{13}{26}$ can be reduced to lowest terms by dividing both numerator and denominator by____.

$\frac{3}{4}$

85. Various forms can be used to show the reduction of fractions to lower terms. Thus,

$$\frac{6}{8} = \frac{3 \cdot 2}{4 \cdot 2} = \frac{3}{4}\left(\frac{2}{2}\right) = \frac{3}{4}(1) = \frac{3}{4},$$

$$\frac{6}{8} = \frac{3 \cdot 2}{4 \cdot 2} = \frac{3}{4},$$

$$\frac{6}{8} = \frac{6 \div 2}{8 \div 2} = \frac{3}{4}, \text{ and}$$

$$\frac{\overset{3}{\cancel{6}}}{\underset{4}{\cancel{8}}} = \frac{3}{4}$$

represent the reduction of $\frac{6}{8}$ to ____ .

$\frac{1}{3} + \frac{1}{4}$

704. If one man takes eight days to complete a certain job, and a second man takes six days to complete the same job, then in one day the first man does $\frac{1}{8}$ of the job, and the second man does $\frac{1}{6}$ of the job. If they work together, then they would complete $\frac{1}{8} + \frac{1}{6}$ of the job. Similarly, if one man takes three days to do a certain job and another man takes four days to do the same job, then, working together, in one day they complete _____ of the job.

$\frac{1}{x}$

705. If one man takes eight days to do a certain job and a second man takes six days to do the same job, how many days will it take them to complete the job if they work together? If x is the number of days it takes them to complete the job working together, then together they complete _____ of the job in one day.

$\frac{1}{8} + \frac{1}{6} = \frac{1}{x}$

706. Two men working together can do $\left(\frac{1}{8} + \frac{1}{6}\right)$ part of a job in one day. They can also do $\frac{1}{x}$ part of the job in one day where x represents the number of days to do the whole job. Equating the two expressions that represent the part of the job done in one day leads to the equation _____ = _____ .

$\frac{24}{7}$

707. The solution of $\frac{1}{8} + \frac{1}{6} = \frac{1}{x}$ is _____ .

$\frac{24}{7}$

708. Since $\frac{24}{7}$ is the solution of $\frac{1}{8} + \frac{1}{6} = \frac{1}{x}$, the number of days required for both men working together to complete the job as described in Frame 705 is _____ days.

$\dfrac{2}{3}$

86. $\dfrac{16}{24} = \dfrac{2 \cdot 8}{3 \cdot 8} = $ ____ .

8

87. $\dfrac{\overset{2}{\cancel{16}}}{\underset{3}{\cancel{24}}} = \dfrac{2}{3}$, where 16 and 24 have each been divided

by ____ .

$\dfrac{5}{7}$

88. Reduce $\dfrac{15}{21}$ to lowest terms.

Remark. The processes used to reduce arithmetic fractions to lowest terms are equally applicable to fractions whose numerators and denominators involve variables.

lowest

89. Algebraic fractions such as $\dfrac{x}{2}, \dfrac{y}{3}, \dfrac{2}{a+1}$ are said to be in "lowest terms" when the numerator and denominator contain no integral or polynomial factors in common. Thus, $\dfrac{x}{2}$ is in _____ terms.

a

90. $\dfrac{a^2 b}{ac}$ is not in lowest terms because both the numerator and denominator contain the common factor ____ .

$\dfrac{ab}{c}$

91. $\dfrac{a^2 b}{ac}$ can be reduced to an equal fraction in lowest terms as follows: $\dfrac{a^2 b}{ac} = \dfrac{ab}{c}\left(\dfrac{a}{a}\right) = \dfrac{ab}{c}(1) = $ _____ .

lowest terms

92. Because both the numerator and denominator contain the common factor $2y^2 z$, $\dfrac{4y^2 z}{6y^3 z^2}$ is not in

_____ _____ .

2

You first have
$\frac{4}{r} + \frac{10}{20r} = \frac{9}{4}$, where r
represents the rate
walking.

700. A man rides 10 miles in a car and then walks 4 miles on foot. If his rate driving is 20 times his rate walking and the whole trip takes $2\frac{1}{4}$ hours, his rate walking is _____ miles per hour.

Remark. The next type of situation we wish to consider is a very common one. It has to do with any process that takes place at a constant rate, and the equations involved in such situations generally make use of the following notion: If a certain event takes k units of time to occur, then the amount of the event that occurs over one unit of time is $\frac{1}{k}$. You find such events in many settings, although we shall consider only one here.

$\frac{1}{6}$

701. Assuming that a man produces work at a constant rate, if a certain job takes him eight days to complete, then in one day he completes $\frac{1}{8}$ of the job. Similarly, if the same job takes another man six days to complete, then in one day he completes _____ of the job.

$\frac{1}{3}$

702. If two men working together can complete a job in three days, then in one day they can complete _____ of the job.

$\frac{1}{x}$

703. If it takes two men working together x days to complete a job, then in one day they complete _____ of the job.

$\dfrac{2}{3yz}$

93. $\dfrac{4y^2z}{6y^3z^2}$ can be reduced to lowest terms as follows:

$$\dfrac{4y^2z}{6y^3z^2} = \dfrac{2}{3yz}\left(\dfrac{2y^2z}{2y^2z}\right) = \dfrac{2}{3yz}(1) = \underline{\hspace{1cm}}.$$

$\dfrac{2x}{y}$

94. $\dfrac{2xy}{y^2} = \dfrac{2x}{y}\left(\dfrac{y}{y}\right) = \underline{\hspace{1cm}}.$

divided

95. $\dfrac{2xy}{y^2}$ can be reduced as follows: $\dfrac{2xy \div y}{y^2 \div y} = \dfrac{2x}{y}$, where the numerator and denominator have each been $\underline{\hspace{2cm}}$ by the common factor y.

$\dfrac{2x}{y}$

96. The division of the numerator and denominator of $\dfrac{2xy}{y^2}$ by the common factor y can be indicated by using the slant bar, $/$.

$$\dfrac{2x\overset{1}{\cancel{y}}}{\underset{y}{\cancel{y^2}}} = \underline{\hspace{1cm}}.$$

$\dfrac{2x}{y}$

97. Various forms can be used to show the reduction of fractions to lower terms. Thus,

$$\dfrac{2xy}{y^2} = \dfrac{2x}{y}\left(\dfrac{y}{y}\right) = \dfrac{2x}{y}(1) = \dfrac{2x}{y},$$

$$\dfrac{2xy}{y^2} = \dfrac{2x \cdot y}{y \cdot y} = \dfrac{2x}{y},$$

$$\dfrac{2xy}{y^2} = \dfrac{2xy \div y}{y^2 \div y} = \dfrac{2x}{y}, \text{ and}$$

$$\dfrac{2x\overset{1}{\cancel{y}}}{\underset{y}{\cancel{y^2}}} = \dfrac{2x}{y}$$

represent the reduction of $\dfrac{2xy}{y^2}$ to the equal fraction

$\underline{\hspace{1cm}}.$

40; 60

If $r = 40$, then $r + 20 = 60$.

695. Since 40 is the solution of the equation $\dfrac{120}{r} = \dfrac{180}{r + 20}$, the rate of the freight train is

_____ miles per hour and the rate of the express train is _____ miles per hour.

$\dfrac{210}{r} = \dfrac{630}{r + 120}$

$\dfrac{210}{r}$ is the time traveled by

the automobile and $\dfrac{630}{r + 120}$ is the time traveled by the airplane.

696. An airplane travels 630 miles in the same time that an automobile travels 210 miles. If the speed of the airplane is 120 miles per hour greater than the speed of the automobile, the condition that the times are equal can be expressed in terms of the rate (r) of

the automobile by the equation _____ .

60

697. The solution of $\dfrac{210}{r} = \dfrac{630}{r + 120}$ is _____ .

60; 180

If r is 60 miles per hour, then $r + 120$ miles per hour is 180 miles per hour.

698. Since the solution of $\dfrac{210}{r} = \dfrac{630}{r + 120}$ is 60, the rate of the automobile in Frame 696 is _____ miles per hour and the rate of the airplane is _____ miles per hour.

$\dfrac{7}{4}$

You first have $\dfrac{7}{r} = \dfrac{15}{r + 2}$, where r represents the rate walking.

699. A man rides 15 miles on his bicycle in the same time it takes him to walk 7 miles. If his rate riding is 2 miles per hour more than his rate walking, his

rate walking is _____ miles per hour.

$\dfrac{x}{2}$

98. $\dfrac{3x^2}{6x} = \dfrac{x}{2}\left(\dfrac{3x}{3x}\right) = \underline{\quad}$.

$\dfrac{1}{x}$

99. Reduce $\dfrac{x}{x^2}$ to lowest terms.

$\dfrac{1}{x^2}$

100. Reduce $\dfrac{x^2}{x^4}$ to lowest terms.

$\dfrac{y}{x}$

101. Reduce $\dfrac{xy}{x^2}$ to lowest terms.

$4x$

102. $\dfrac{4x^2}{x} = 4x\left(\dfrac{x}{x}\right) = \underline{\quad}$.

$2xy$

103. $\dfrac{8xy^2}{4y} = \underline{\quad\quad}$.

$3x^2y$

104. $\dfrac{3x^3y^2}{xy} = \underline{\quad\quad}$.

Remark. The important thing to remember from the material you have covered to this point is the fundamental principle of fractions, in the form

$$\frac{a}{b} = \frac{ac}{bc} \quad \text{or} \quad \frac{ac}{bc} = \frac{a}{b}.$$

This principle is used over and over again in working with fractions.

The next sequence of frames will extend the application of the fundamental principle of fractions to fractions with more complicated numerators and denominators. In order to be able to do the work satisfactorily, you will have to be able to factor polynomials. If you cannot do this, the few review frames located along the way will not be of too much help, and you should first go back and work through Unit IV of Programmed Beginning Algebra before continuing with this unit.

time

689. Suppose a freight train travels 120 miles in the same length of time an express train travels 180 miles, and suppose that the express travels 20 miles per hour faster than the freight; how fast must each be traveling? Since the <u>time</u> the trains travel is the same in each case, it seems reasonable to approach the problem by writing an equation relating the_____ each travels.

$r + 20$

690. If r represents the rate of the freight, and if the express travels 20 miles per hour faster than the freight, the rate of the express is given in terms of r by _____ .

$\dfrac{120}{r}$

$t = \dfrac{d}{r}.$

691. If the freight train travels 120 miles at a rate (r), the time it takes to do this can be represented by the expression _____ .

$\dfrac{180}{r + 20}$

$t = \dfrac{d}{r}.$

692. If the express train travels 180 miles at a rate $(r + 20)$, the time it takes to do this can be represented by the expression _____ .

$\dfrac{120}{r} = \dfrac{180}{r + 20}$

693. The fact that the time traveled by the freight train and the time traveled by the express train is the same, can be expressed in terms of r by the equation _____ = _____ .

40

694. The solution of $\dfrac{120}{r} = \dfrac{180}{r + 20}$ is _____ .

distributive

105. Recall that the distributive law is written

$$a(b + c) = ab + ac \quad \text{or} \quad ab + ac = a(b + c).$$

This law asserts that monomial factors common to each term in a polynomial can be factored from the polynomial. Thus, writing $3a + 3 = 3(a + 1)$ is an application of the_____law.

$a + 2b$

106. By the distributive law, $4a + 8b = 4(\underline{\quad\quad})$.

$3a$

107. By the distributive law, $3a^2 + 6a = \underline{\quad}(a + 2)$.

$\dfrac{a - 1}{3}$

108. Fractions whose numerators or denominators contain more than one term can be reduced to lowest terms by first completely factoring the numerator and denominator. Thus, $\dfrac{2a + 2}{6} = \dfrac{2(a + 1)}{2 \cdot 3} = \left(\dfrac{2}{2}\right)\dfrac{a + 1}{3} = \dfrac{a + 1}{3}$.

Similarly, $\dfrac{5a - 5}{15} = \dfrac{5(a - 1)}{5 \cdot 3} = \left(\dfrac{5}{5}\right)\dfrac{a - 1}{3} = \underline{\qquad\qquad}$.

$\dfrac{a + 2}{2}$

109. $\dfrac{3a + 6}{6} = \dfrac{3(a + 2)}{3 \cdot 2} = \underline{\qquad\qquad}$.

$\dfrac{1 + 2a}{7}$

110. Reduce $\dfrac{4 + 8a}{28}$ to lowest terms.

You first have $\dfrac{4(1 + 2a)}{4 \cdot 7}$.

$\dfrac{a + 1}{3}$

111. $\dfrac{a^2 + a}{3a} = \dfrac{a(a + 1)}{3a} = \underline{\qquad\qquad}$.

$x + x + \dfrac{2}{3}x = 16$

A sketch would appear as

684. The perimeter of a triangle with two equal sides is 16 inches. The length of the third side is two thirds the length of one of the equal sides. If x represents the length of one of the equal sides, an equation stating the condition placed on x by this sentence can be written as

_____

6

685. The solution of $x + x + \dfrac{2}{3}x = 16$ is_____.

6 feet; 6 feet; 4 feet

If x is 6, then $\dfrac{2}{3}x$ is 4.

686. The three sides of the triangle in Frame 684 are_____, _____ , and _____.

8 feet; 3 feet

You first have the equation
$x + \dfrac{3}{8}x + x + \dfrac{3}{8}x = 22.$

687. The width of a rectangle is $\dfrac{3}{8}$ of the length. If the perimeter is 22 feet, the length is_____and the width is_____.

$t = \dfrac{d}{r}$

Each member of $d = rt$ is divided by r.

688. The distance (d) traveled in a certain length of time (t) at a constant rate (r) is given by $d = rt$. The time (t) can be represented in terms of the distance and rate by the equation $t = $ _____ .

$$\frac{3a - 1}{4}$$

You first have $\frac{a(3a - 1)}{4a}$.

112. $\frac{3a^2 - a}{4a} = $ _____ .

$$\frac{1 - 2a}{3}$$

113. $\frac{3a - 6a^2}{9a} = \frac{3a(1 - 2a)}{3 \cdot 3a} = $ _____ .

$$\frac{1 + 3a}{2}$$

$$\frac{4a(1 + 3a)}{2 \cdot 4a} .$$

114. Reduce $\frac{4a + 12a^2}{8a}$ to lowest terms.

$$\frac{x - 2}{3x - 2}$$

115. $\frac{2x - 4}{6x - 4} = \frac{2(x - 2)}{2(3x - 2)} = $ _____ .

$$\frac{2(1 + 2x)}{1 - 3x}$$

Or $\frac{2 + 4x}{1 - 3x}$.

You first have $\frac{2 \cdot 2(1 + 2x)}{2(1 - 3x)}$.

116. Reduce $\frac{4 + 8x}{2 - 6x}$.

$$\frac{2}{3}$$

117. $\frac{2x + 2}{3x + 3} = \frac{2(x + 1)}{3(x + 1)} = $ _____ .

$$\frac{3}{4}$$

You first have $\frac{3(2 - x)}{4(2 - x)}$.

118. Reduce $\frac{6 - 3x}{8 - 4x}$.

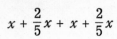

$x + \dfrac{2}{5}x + x + \dfrac{2}{5}x$

A sketch proves helpful in matters such as this.

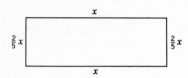

679. If x represents the length of a rectangle and $\dfrac{2}{5}x$ represents the width, the phrase "the perimeter (sum of the four sides) of the rectangle" can be represented by

_____ .

$x + \dfrac{2}{5}x + x + \dfrac{2}{5}x = 112$

680. The perimeter of a rectangle is 112 feet. If x represents a length of a rectangle and the width is two fifths of the length, the equation relating the conditions on the variable x can be written as

_____ .

40

681. The solution of $x + \dfrac{2}{5}x + x + \dfrac{2}{5}x = 112$ is _____ .

16

682. If x (representing the length of the rectangle in Frame 680) is 40, then $\dfrac{2}{5}x$ (representing the width) is _____ .

40 feet; 16 feet

The units are feet.

683. The length of the rectangle in Frame 680 is _____ feet and the width is _____ feet.

Remark. Solutions of equations are numbers. However, solutions of word problems are often not numbers alone, but measures of things; feet, pounds, dollars, and the like. In giving your solution of a word problem, you should be careful that you do not simply write down whatever solution or solutions your equation may have. Answers to word problems should be stated so that they make sense within the context of the problem itself. You use your equation to obtain a number or some numbers, but it is up to you to interpret these numbers in the light of what the problem asks of you.

$\dfrac{x}{3}$

119. $\dfrac{2x^2 + x}{6x + 3} = \dfrac{x(2x + 1)}{3(2x + 1)} = $ _____ .

$\dfrac{x}{2}$

120. $\dfrac{x - 5x^2}{2 - 10x} = $ _____ .

$\dfrac{x(1 - 5x)}{2(1 - 5x)}.$

$\dfrac{1}{x - 1}$

121. $\dfrac{x + 3}{(x - 1)(x + 3)} = \dfrac{1}{x - 1} \cdot \dfrac{x + 3}{x + 3} = $ _____ .

$\dfrac{1}{x + 4}$

122. $\dfrac{x - 2}{(x - 2)(x + 4)} = $ _____ .

$(x - 1)(x - 2)$

123. Recall that some trinomials can be factored into a product of two binomials. For example,
$x^2 + 3x + 2 = (x + 1)(x + 2)$, and
$x^2 - 3x + 2 = ($ _____ $)($ _____ $)$.

$(x - 4)(x + 1)$

124. $x^2 - 3x - 4 = ($ _____ $)($ _____ $)$.

$\dfrac{1}{x + 1}$

125. $\dfrac{x + 1}{x^2 + 2x + 1} = \dfrac{x + 1}{(x + 1)(x + 1)} = $ _____ .

$\dfrac{1}{x - 3}$

126. $\dfrac{x - 1}{x^2 - 4x + 3} = $ _____ .

$\dfrac{(x - 1)}{(x - 1)(x - 3)}$

is

The sum of half of five
and three times five
does equal $\frac{35}{2}$.

672. 5 is a solution of $\frac{1}{2}x + 3x = \frac{35}{2}$.   5 (is/is not) a solution of the word problem in Frame 670.

$\frac{2}{3}(x + 5) = 12$

673. If x represents a number, the sentence "two thirds of the sum of a certain number and 5 equals 12" can be represented by the equation

_____ .

13

674. The solution of $\frac{2}{3}(x + 5) = 12$ is_____ .

---

is

675. 13 (is/is not) a solution of the word problem in Frame 673.

6

You first have the equation
$\frac{2x}{x - 2} = 3$, where x
represents the number.

676. If twice a certain number is divided by 2 less than the number, the result is 3. The number is_____ .

18

You first have the equation
$\frac{x}{x + 6} = \frac{3}{4}$, where x
represents the numerator.

677. If the denominator of a certain fraction is six more than the numerator, and the fraction is equal to $\frac{3}{4}$, the numerator is_____ .

$\frac{2}{5}x$

Or $\frac{2x}{5}$.

678. If x represents the length of a rectangle and the width is two fifths of the length, the width can be represented in terms of x by _____ .

$$\frac{1}{x+1}$$

$$\frac{(x+4)}{(x+4)(x+1)}$$

$x + 2$

$x - 1$

$$\frac{x+2}{x+4}$$

$$\frac{x-2}{x-7}$$

$$\frac{x-1}{x+1}$$

$$\frac{x-1}{x+3}$$

$$\frac{x-2}{x+2}$$

127. $\dfrac{x+4}{x^2+5x+4} = $ _____ .

128. $\dfrac{x^2+4x+4}{x+2} = $ _____ .

129. $\dfrac{x^2-6x+5}{x-5} = $ _____ .

130. $\dfrac{x^2+3x+2}{x^2+5x+4} = \dfrac{(x+2)(x+1)}{(x+4)(x+1)} = $ _____ .

131. $\dfrac{x^2-3x+2}{x^2-8x+7} = $ _____ .

132. $\dfrac{x^2-1}{x^2+2x+1} = $ _____ .

133. $\dfrac{x^2-4x+3}{x^2-9} = $ _____ .

134. $\dfrac{x^2-4}{(x+2)^2} = $ _____ .

Remark. The word "simplify" is often used to shorten the directions "reduce to lowest terms."

-2

666. Solve $\dfrac{1}{3} = \dfrac{x+3}{x+5}$.

2

667. Solve $\dfrac{1}{2} = \dfrac{x}{6-x}$.

Remark. Fractional equations have many kinds of applications. The next sequence of frames will introduce you to a few of them.

$\dfrac{1}{2}x$

Or $\dfrac{x}{2}$.

668. If x represents a number, then half the number can be represented by _____ .

$\dfrac{1}{2}x + 3x$

669. If x represents a number, then the phrase "the sum of half of a number and three times the number" can be represented by the expression _____ .

$\dfrac{1}{2}x + 3x = \dfrac{35}{2}$

670. If x represents a number, then the sentence "the sum of half of a number and three times the number equals $\dfrac{35}{2}$" can be represented by the equation _____ .

5

671. The solution of $\dfrac{1}{2}x + 3x = \dfrac{35}{2}$ is _____ .

$$\frac{2}{y + 2}$$

135. Simplify: $\dfrac{2y - 4}{y^2 - 4}$.

$$\frac{x - 4}{x + 2}$$

136. Simplify: $\dfrac{x^2 - 6x + 8}{x^2 - 4}$.

$$\frac{x + 4}{x + 1}$$

137. Simplify: $\dfrac{x^2 + 5x + 4}{(x + 1)^2}$.

$$\frac{x}{x - 3}$$

138. Simplify: $\dfrac{x^2 - x}{x^2 - 4x + 3}$.

Remark. You have now learned to reduce fractions of certain kinds to lowest terms by applying the fundamental principle of fractions. Your next task will be to learn to change fractions from one form to another equal form by altering the signs associated with a fraction.

$+ ; -$

139. There are three signs associated with a fraction, the sign of the numerator, the sign of the denominator, and the sign of the fraction itself. The sign associated with the numerator of the fraction $-\dfrac{+2}{-3}$ is____. The sign associated with the denominator is____.

140. The sign associated with the fraction $-\dfrac{a}{b}$ is____.

1

141. Because the quotient of two negative integers is a positive integer, the value of $\dfrac{-3}{-3}$ is 1. The value of $\dfrac{-1}{-1}$ is____.

(6)(8)

Or (8)(6).

657. If $\dfrac{x}{8} = \dfrac{6}{16}$, then $16x = (\underline{\quad})(\underline{\quad})$.

3

You first have $16x = 48$.

658. The solution of $16x = (6)(8)$ is _____.

(3)(8)

659. If $\dfrac{3}{4} = \dfrac{1+y}{8}$, then $\underline{(\quad)}\underline{(\quad)} = 4(1 + y)$.

5

You first have $24 = 4 + 4y$, and then $20 = 4y$.

660. The solution of $(3)(8) = 4(1 + y)$ is _____.

$(2)(y + 2)$

661. If $\dfrac{y}{y+2} = \dfrac{2}{3}$, then $3y = (\underline{\quad})(\underline{\qquad})$.

4

662. The solution of $3y = 2(y + 2)$ is _____.

9

663. Solve $\dfrac{3}{4} = \dfrac{y}{y+3}$.

$\dfrac{3}{13}$

664. Solve $\dfrac{2y}{3} = \dfrac{y+1}{8}$.

7

665. Solve $\dfrac{x}{x-2} = \dfrac{14}{10}$.

−2

$\frac{5}{7}$

142. Because $\frac{-1}{-1}$ is equal to 1, multiplying $\frac{a}{b}$ by $\frac{-1}{-1}$ produces an equal fraction. That is $\frac{a}{b}\left(\frac{-1}{-1}\right) = \frac{-a}{-b}$, $\frac{2}{3} = \frac{-2}{-3}$, and $\frac{-2}{-3} = \frac{2}{3}$. Similarly, $\frac{-5}{-7} = $ _____.

$\frac{8}{11}$

143. $\frac{-1}{-1}$ is equal to $(-1)\left(\frac{1}{-1}\right)$, and hence $(-1)\left(\frac{1}{-1}\right)$ is equal to 1. Therefore, multiplying $\frac{a}{b}$ by $(-1)\left(\frac{1}{-1}\right)$ produces an equal fraction. That is $\frac{a}{b}(-1)\left(\frac{1}{-1}\right) = -\frac{a}{-b}$, $\frac{2}{3} = -\frac{2}{-3}$, and $-\frac{2}{-3} = \frac{2}{3}$. Similarly, $-\frac{8}{-11} = $ _____.

$\frac{3}{4}$

144. $\frac{-1}{-1}$ is equal to $(-1)\left(\frac{-1}{1}\right)$, and hence $(-1)\left(\frac{-1}{1}\right)$ is equal to 1. Therefore, multiplying $\frac{a}{b}$ by $(-1)\left(\frac{-1}{1}\right)$ produces an equal fraction. That is, $\frac{a}{b}(-1)\left(\frac{-1}{1}\right) = -\frac{-a}{b}$, $\frac{6}{13} = -\frac{-6}{13}$, and $-\frac{-6}{13} = \frac{6}{13}$. Similarly, $-\frac{-3}{4} = $ _____.

two

145. The ideas contained in the preceding three frames lead to the principle:

> *If any two of the three signs associated with a fraction are changed, the resulting fraction is equal to the original fraction.*

Thus, $\frac{-3}{-5} = \frac{3}{5}$, because _____ of the three signs associated with $\frac{-3}{-5}$ have been changed.

numerator

146. The fraction $-\frac{5}{7}$ can be written as the equal fraction $\frac{-5}{7}$ by changing the sign on the fraction and the sign on the _____.

$(bd)\dfrac{c}{d}$

651. The LCD of the fractions in $\dfrac{a}{b} = \dfrac{c}{d}$ is bd, and the equation can be written as the equivalent equation $(bd)\dfrac{a}{b} = \underline{\hspace{2cm}}\dfrac{c}{d}$.

bc

652. $(bd)\dfrac{a}{b} = (bd)\dfrac{c}{d}$ can be written in simpler form as $ad = \underline{\hspace{2cm}}$.

$(1)(6) = (2)(3)$

653. $\dfrac{a}{b} = \dfrac{c}{d}$ can be transformed to the equivalent equation $ad = bc$. This transformation can be expressed:

> *In any proportion, the product of the extremes equals the product of the means.*

Thus, $\dfrac{1}{2} = \dfrac{3}{6}$ can be written as the equivalent statement $(1)(6) = \underline{\hspace{2cm}}$.

extremes; means

654. $\dfrac{3}{4} = \dfrac{6}{8}$ can be written as the equivalent statement $(3)(8) = (4)(6)$ because, in any proportion, the product of the _____ equals the product of the _____.

$(3)(4); \ (3)(4)$

655. $\dfrac{2}{3} = \dfrac{4}{6}$. The product of the extremes is $(2)(6)$ and the product of the means is _____.
Therefore, $(2)(6) = (\ \ \ )(\ \ \ )$.

extremes; means

656. $\dfrac{4}{7} = \dfrac{8}{14}$. The product of the _____ is $(4)(14)$ and the product of the _____ is $(7)(8)$.
Therefore, $(4)(14) = (7)(8)$.

denominator

147. The fraction $\dfrac{-5}{-12}$ can be written as the equal fraction $\dfrac{5}{12}$ by changing two signs, the sign on the numerator and the sign on the _____.

fraction

148. The fraction $-\dfrac{5}{-12}$ can be written as the equal fraction $\dfrac{5}{12}$ by changing the sign on the denominator and the sign on the _____ itself.

numerator

149. $-\dfrac{-5}{12}$ can be written as the equal fraction $\dfrac{5}{12}$ by changing the sign on the fraction and the sign on the _____.

$\dfrac{5}{12}$; positive

150. $\dfrac{-5}{-12}$, $-\dfrac{5}{-12}$, and $-\dfrac{-5}{12}$ can all be written as the equal fraction _____. Each of these represents a (positive/negative) number.

denominator

151. The fraction $\dfrac{5}{-12}$ can be written as the equal fraction $\dfrac{-5}{12}$ by changing two signs, the sign on the numerator and the sign on the _____.

fraction

152. The fraction $-\dfrac{5}{12}$ can be written as the equal fraction $\dfrac{-5}{12}$ by changing the sign on the numerator and the sign on the _____itself.

8

6

extremes

means

means

extremes

4

3; y

Or y; 3.

643. In a proportion of the form $\frac{a}{b} = \frac{c}{d}$, the numbers a, b, c, and d are called the first, second, third, and fourth terms, respectively. In the proportion $\frac{3}{4} = \frac{6}{8}$, the first term is 3 and the fourth term is _____.

644. In the proportion $\frac{3}{4} = \frac{6}{8}$, the second term is 4 and the third term is_____.

645. In a proportion the first and fourth terms are called the extremes. If $\frac{a}{b} = \frac{c}{d}$ then a and d are called the_____.

646. In a proportion the second and third terms are called the means. If $\frac{a}{b} = \frac{c}{d}$, then b and c are the_____.

647. In $\frac{3}{4} = \frac{6}{8}$, 3 and 8 are the extremes and 4 and 6 are the_____.

648. If $\frac{3}{x} = \frac{12}{16}$, 3 and 16 are the_____ and x and 12 are the means.

649. If $\frac{y}{2} = \frac{8 + y}{4}$, the extremes are y and_____.

650. If $\frac{y + 1}{3} = \frac{y}{4}$, the means are_____ and _____.

denominator

153. $-\dfrac{-5}{-12}$ can be written as the equal fraction $\dfrac{-5}{12}$ by changing the sign on the fraction and the sign on the _____ .

$\dfrac{-5}{12}$; negative

154. $\dfrac{5}{-12}$, $-\dfrac{5}{12}$, and $-\dfrac{-5}{-12}$ can be written as the equal fraction _____ . Each of these fractions represents a (positive/negative) number.

negative

155. Any fraction is equal to a fraction either of the form $\dfrac{a}{b}$ or $-\dfrac{a}{b}$. If a and b are positive, $\dfrac{a}{b}$ represents a positive number, and $-\dfrac{a}{b}$ represents a _____ number.

negative

156. Since $\dfrac{-3}{4}$ is equal to $-\dfrac{3}{4}$, $\dfrac{-3}{4}$ represents a _____ number.

positive

157. Since $-\dfrac{-3}{4}$ is equal to $\dfrac{3}{4}$, $-\dfrac{-3}{4}$ represents a _____ number.

negative

Both are equal to $-\dfrac{7}{8}$.

158. The fraction $\dfrac{7}{-8}$ equals $\dfrac{-7}{8}$, and both represent a _____ number.

positive

159. $\dfrac{-7}{-8} = \dfrac{7}{8}$, and both represent a _____ number.

4

637. Solve $\dfrac{4}{15y} - \dfrac{2-y}{5y} = \dfrac{1}{6}$.

2

638. Solve $\dfrac{2}{y+4} = \dfrac{2}{3y}$.

2

639. Solve $\dfrac{3}{2y-1} = \dfrac{7}{3y+1}$.

Remark. We next consider a special type of fractional equation that is widely encountered in mathematics and in areas of applied mathematics.

ratio

640. The quotient of two numbers, $a \div b$ or $\dfrac{a}{b}$, is sometimes referred to as a ratio and read "the ratio of a to b." The quotient $\dfrac{3}{4}$ can be read "the _____ of 3 to 4."

proportion

641. A statement that two ratios are equal, for example $\dfrac{a}{b} = \dfrac{c}{d}$, is called a proportion and is read "a is to b as c is to d." $\dfrac{3}{4}$ and $\dfrac{6}{8}$ are equal ratios and the statement $\dfrac{3}{4} = \dfrac{6}{8}$ is a _____ .

proportion

642. $\dfrac{1}{2}$ is a ratio. $\dfrac{1}{2} = \dfrac{2}{4}$ is a _____ .

$-\dfrac{7}{-8}$; $\dfrac{-7}{-8}$; $-\dfrac{-7}{8}$

160. The members of $\left\{\dfrac{7}{-8}, -\dfrac{7}{-8}, \dfrac{-7}{-8}, -\dfrac{-7}{8}, -\dfrac{7}{8}, -\dfrac{-7}{-8}\right\}$ that are equal to the fraction $\dfrac{7}{8}$ are _____ , _____ , and _____ .

$\dfrac{7}{-8}$; $-\dfrac{7}{8}$; $-\dfrac{-7}{-8}$

161. The members of $\left\{\dfrac{7}{-8}, -\dfrac{7}{-8}, \dfrac{-7}{-8}, -\dfrac{-7}{8}, -\dfrac{7}{8}, -\dfrac{-7}{-8}\right\}$ that are equal to the fraction $\dfrac{-7}{8}$ are _____ , _____ , and _____ .

$\dfrac{-4}{-5}$; $-\dfrac{4}{-5}$; $-\dfrac{-4}{5}$

162. The members of $\left\{\dfrac{4}{-5}, \dfrac{-4}{-5}, -\dfrac{4}{5}, -\dfrac{4}{-5}, -\dfrac{-4}{-5}, -\dfrac{-4}{5}\right\}$ that are equal to $\dfrac{4}{5}$ are _____ , _____ , and _____ .

$\dfrac{4}{-5}$; $-\dfrac{4}{5}$; $-\dfrac{-4}{-5}$

163. The members of $\left\{\dfrac{4}{-5}, \dfrac{-4}{-5}, -\dfrac{4}{5}, -\dfrac{4}{-5}, -\dfrac{-4}{-5}, -\dfrac{-4}{5}\right\}$ that are equal to $\dfrac{-4}{5}$ are _____ , _____ , and _____ .

is

164. A fraction with a positive sign on the denominator and a positive sign on the fraction such as $\dfrac{-a}{b}$ or $\dfrac{a}{b}$ is the most convenient form of a fraction to use. A fraction in this form is said to be in standard form. Thus, $\dfrac{3}{4}$ is in standard form, but $-\dfrac{3}{-4}, -\dfrac{-3}{4},$ and $\dfrac{-3}{-4}$ are not. $\dfrac{5}{6}$ (is/is not) in standard form.

is not

The denominator is negative.

165. $\dfrac{-5}{-6}$ (is/is not) in standard form.

1

You first have
$4x + 5 = 6 + 3x$.

629. The solution of $2 + \dfrac{5}{2x} = \dfrac{3}{x} + \dfrac{3}{2}$ is_____.

$5(x + 2)$

630. The LCD of the fractions in

$\dfrac{3}{5} = \dfrac{x}{x + 2}$ is_____.

$(x + 2)3 = 5x$

Again, we assume that
$x + 2$ is not equal to 0.
That is, we assume x is
not equal to -2. From
now on, such restrictions
will be assumed without
stating them.

631. Multiplying each member of $\dfrac{3}{5} = \dfrac{x}{x + 2}$ by

$[(5)(x + 2)]$ yields $(5)(x + 2)\dfrac{3}{5} = (5)(x + 2)\dfrac{x}{x + 2}$.
In simpler form the equation appears as
$(x + 2)3 = $ _____.

3

632. The solution of $(x + 2)3 = 5x$ is_____.

$(x + 10)(x + 3)$

633. The LCD of the fractions in the equation

$\dfrac{2}{x + 10} = \dfrac{1}{x + 3}$ is_____.

4

634. The solution of $\dfrac{2}{x + 10} = \dfrac{1}{x + 3}$ is_____.

$\dfrac{5}{6}$

635. Solve $1 + \dfrac{1}{2x} = \dfrac{4}{3x}$.

$\dfrac{41}{3}$

636. Solve $1 - \dfrac{2}{3x} = \dfrac{13}{x}$.

is

166. $\frac{-5}{9}$ is in standard form, while $\frac{5}{-9}$, $-\frac{5}{9}$, and $-\frac{-5}{-9}$ are not in standard form. $\frac{-4}{7}$ (is/is not) in standard form.

is

167. $\frac{-8}{9}$ (is/is not) in standard form.

is not

168. $-\frac{8}{9}$ (is/is not) in standard form.

equal

169. To write $-\frac{2}{3}$ as a fraction in standard form, two signs are changed, the sign on the fraction and the sign on the numerator. Thus, $-\frac{2}{3}$ is written in standard form as $\frac{-2}{3}$. If any two signs associated with a fraction are changed, the result is an equal fraction. Thus, $-\frac{2}{3}$ is _____ to $\frac{-2}{3}$.

numerator; fraction

170. $-\frac{-3}{4}$ can be written in the standard form $\frac{3}{4}$ by changing the signs on the _____ and the _____ itself.

numerator; denominator

Or vice versa.

171. $\frac{3}{-4}$ can be written in the standard form $\frac{-3}{4}$ by changing the signs on the _____ and the _____.

$\frac{-7}{3}$

172. Changing the signs on the numerator and the fraction itself, $-\frac{7}{3}$ can be written in standard form ____.

$\dfrac{17}{3}$

You first have
$x + 11 - 22 + 2x = 6$,
and then $3x = 17$.

623. The equation $\dfrac{x + 11}{6} - \dfrac{11 - x}{3} = 1$ can be written

as $\dfrac{x + 11}{6} + \dfrac{-(11 - x)}{3} = 1$. Multiplying each member

of this equation by 6 yields

$(6)\dfrac{(x + 11)}{6} + (6)\dfrac{-(11 - x)}{3} = (6)1$. The solution of

any of these equations is _____ .

$-\dfrac{1}{2}$

624. Solve $\dfrac{1}{2} - \dfrac{2x - 2}{2} = 2$.

equivalent

625. One equation can be transformed to an
equivalent equation if each member is multiplied
by the same nonzero number. Thus, if $a = b$,
then $ac = bc$ is an _____ equation for
any value of c except 0.

4

626. If $\dfrac{12}{x} = 3$, and x is not 0, then $(x)\dfrac{12}{x} = (x)3$,
which simplifies to $12 = 3x$. The solution of this
equation is _____ .

x

We assume that x is not
equal to 0.

627. $1 + \dfrac{3}{x} = \dfrac{12}{x}$ can be transformed to an equivalent

equation without fractions by multiplying each
member by _____ .

$2x$

628. The LCD of the fractions in

$2 + \dfrac{5}{2x} = \dfrac{3}{x} + \dfrac{3}{2}$ is _____ .

$\frac{6}{5}$

173. Changing the signs on the numerator and the denominator, $\frac{-6}{-5}$ can be written in standard form _____ .

$\frac{3}{4}$

174. Write $-\frac{3}{-4}$ in standard form.

$\frac{-8}{7}$

175. Write $-\frac{-8}{-7}$ in standard form.

is

176. The algebraic fraction $\frac{a}{b}$ is in standard form, and the fractions $\frac{-a}{-b}$, $-\frac{-a}{b}$, and $-\frac{a}{-b}$ are not. $\frac{x}{y}$ (is/is not) in standard form.

is

177. The algebraic fraction $\frac{-a}{b}$ is in standard form, and the fractions $\frac{a}{-b}$, $-\frac{a}{-b}$, and $-\frac{-a}{-b}$ are not. $\frac{-x}{y}$ (is/is not) in standard form.

$\frac{-3x^2}{y}$

178. Changing the signs on the numerator and the fraction itself, $-\frac{3x^2}{y}$ can be written in standard form

_____ .

$\frac{x^2}{y^3}$

179. Write $-\frac{-x^2}{y^3}$ in standard form.

$\frac{-5x^3}{y}$

180. Write $-\frac{-5x^3}{-y}$ in standard form.

10

614. The LCD of the fractions in

$x - \dfrac{3}{10} = \dfrac{1}{2} + \dfrac{3x}{5}$ is _____.

2

615. The solution of $x - \dfrac{3}{10} = \dfrac{1}{2} + \dfrac{3x}{5}$ is _____.

18

616. The LCD of the fractions in

$\dfrac{y + 12}{9} = \dfrac{y - 9}{2}$ is _____.

15

You first have
$2y + 24 = 9y - 81$ and
then $-7y = -105$.

617. Multiplying each member of $\dfrac{y + 12}{9} = \dfrac{y - 9}{2}$ by 18

yields $(18)\dfrac{(y + 12)}{9} = (18)\dfrac{(y - 9)}{2}$ or $2(y + 12) = 9(y - 9)$.

The solution of any of these equations is _____.

20

618. The LCD of the fractions in

$\dfrac{y - 5}{4} = \dfrac{2y - 9}{10}$ is _____.

7

619. The solution of $\dfrac{y - 5}{4} = \dfrac{2y - 9}{10}$ is _____.

6

620. The LCD of the fractions in

$\dfrac{2x}{3} - \dfrac{1}{2} = \dfrac{2x + 5}{6}$ is _____.

4

621. The solution of $\dfrac{2x}{3} - \dfrac{1}{2} = \dfrac{2x + 5}{6}$ is _____.

5

622. Solve $\dfrac{x - 1}{10} + \dfrac{19}{15} = \dfrac{x}{3}$.

$\dfrac{-4}{x+1}$

181. Write $-\dfrac{4}{x+1}$ in standard form.

$\dfrac{-5b}{b+1}$

Or $\dfrac{-5b}{(b+1)}$. The parentheses
are not really needed.

182. $\dfrac{3}{-(a+1)}$ appears in standard form as $\dfrac{-3}{a+1}$.

Write $\dfrac{5b}{-(b+1)}$ in standard form.

$\dfrac{2x^2}{x-1}$

183. Write $-\dfrac{2x^2}{-(x-1)}$ in standard form.

$\dfrac{-(b+a)}{ab}$

This time the parentheses
are necessary.

184. $\dfrac{a+1}{-a}$ appears in standard form as $\dfrac{-(a+1)}{a}$.

Write $\dfrac{b+a}{-ab}$ in standard form.

$\dfrac{-(a+1)}{a}$

185. Write $-\dfrac{a+1}{a}$ in standard form.

$\dfrac{a+2b}{b}$

186. Write $-\dfrac{a+2b}{-b}$ in standard form.

$(x-y)$

187. Notice that $-(a-b) = -a+b = (b-a)$. That is, if a binomial factor of the form $(b-c)$ is written $(c-b)$, the result is the negative of the original binomial. Thus, $(y-x)$ is the negative of (_____).

$(z-3)$

188. $(3-z)$ is the negative of (_____).

4

607. Recall that the least common denominator (LCD) of a set of fractions is the lowest number each denominator will divide into without remainder. Thus, the LCD of $\frac{x}{2}$ and $\frac{x}{4}$ is_____.

common denominator

608. $\frac{x}{2} + \frac{x}{4} = 6$ can be transformed to the equivalent equation $2x + x = 24$ by multiplying each member of the equation by 4, the least _____ _____of the fractions.

8

You first have $3x = 24$.

609. $\frac{x}{2} + \frac{x}{4} = 6$ is equivalent to $2x + x = 24$. The solution of either equation is_____.

6

610. $\frac{2x}{3} - \frac{5x}{6} = 4$ can be transformed to an equivalent equation that does not contain fractions by multiplying each member by_____, the LCD of the fractions.

-24

611. $(6)\frac{2x}{3} - (6)\frac{5x}{6} = (6)4$ can be simplified to $4x - 5x = 24$. The solution of either equation is_____.

6

612. $\frac{x}{2} - \frac{2x}{3} = 5$ can be transformed to an equivalent equation that does not contain fractions by multiplying each member by_____, the LCD of the fractions.

-30

613. The solution of $\frac{x}{2} - \frac{2x}{3} = 5$ is_____.

$(y + 3)$

189. If both terms in a binomial are positive, the commutative law justifies writing an expression such as $(x + y)$ as $(y + x)$. Similarly $(3 + y) = ($ _____ $)$.

$(-c - d)$

190. The negative of $(a + b)$ is $(-a - b)$, where both signs are negative. The negative of $(c + d)$ is $($ _____ $)$.

does

The sign on the numerator and the sign on the denominator have been changed.

$\dfrac{(1 - a)(-1)}{(-a)\,(-1)} = \dfrac{a - 1}{a}$

191. $\dfrac{a - b}{-b}$ appears in standard form as $\dfrac{-(a - b)}{b}$, which can be also represented by other equal fractions such as $\dfrac{-a + b}{b}$ or $\dfrac{b - a}{b}$. $\dfrac{1 - a}{-a}$ (does/does not) equal $\dfrac{a - 1}{a}$.

does

192. $\dfrac{2x - y}{-y}$ (does/does not) equal $\dfrac{y - 2x}{y}$.

numerator

193. $-\dfrac{x - 3}{2}$ can be written in standard form as $\dfrac{3 - x}{2}$, where the sign on the fraction itself and the sign on the _____ have been changed.

$\dfrac{x - 3}{5}$

194. Write $-\dfrac{3 - x}{5}$ in standard form.

$\dfrac{x - y}{7}$

195. Write $-\dfrac{y - x}{7}$ in standard form.

$\dfrac{2}{x - 3}$

$\dfrac{-2}{3 - x}$ is also acceptable.

196. $-\dfrac{4}{5 - y}$ can be written in standard form as $\dfrac{4}{y - 5}$ or $\dfrac{-4}{5 - y}$. Write $-\dfrac{2}{3 - x}$ in standard form.

2

600. $\frac{1}{2}(x + 1) = 6$ can be transformed to the equivalent equation $x + 1 = 12$ by multiplying each member by _____.

11

If the solution is not evident, $x + 1 = 12$ can be transformed to the equivalent equation $x = 11$ by adding -1 to each member.

601. The solution of $x + 1 = 12$ can be obtained by inspection. The solution is _____.

$\frac{1}{2}(x + 1) = 6$

602. Since $\frac{1}{2}(x + 1) = 6$ and $x + 1 = 12$ are equivalent and 11 is the solution of $x + 1 = 12$, 11 is also the solution of _____ = ___ .

3

603. $\frac{x + 4}{3} = -2$ can be transformed to the equivalent equation $x + 4 = -6$ by multiplying each member by _____ .

-10

604. The solution of $x + 4 = -6$ is -10. Therefore, since the equations are equivalent, the solution of $\frac{x + 4}{3} = -2$ is _____.

7

Multiplying each member by 2, you first have $x + 5 = 12$.

605. The solution of $\frac{x + 5}{2} = 6$ is _____.

11

606. The solution of $\frac{1}{3}(x - 5) = 2$ is _____.

$\dfrac{b-a}{b}$

Or, of course, $\dfrac{-(a-b)}{b}$.

197. $\dfrac{a-b}{-b}$, when written in standard form, appears as

_____ .

$\dfrac{3}{x-3}$

Or $\dfrac{-3}{3-x}$.

198. $\dfrac{3}{-(3-x)}$, when written in standard form, appears

as _____ .

Remark. The purpose of designating certain forms of fractions as "standard" and of learning to rewrite fractions in standard form is to make it easier to affect some of the operations that will be performed on fractions a little later. At this time, we shall examine the addition of fractions.

$\dfrac{1}{5}$; $\dfrac{3}{5}$

199. $\dfrac{2}{3} + \dfrac{5}{3}$ represents the sum of $\dfrac{2}{3}$ and $\dfrac{5}{3}$. $\dfrac{1}{5} + \dfrac{3}{5}$ represents the sum of ____ and ____ .

$\dfrac{x}{3}$; $\dfrac{y}{3}$

200. $\dfrac{x}{3} + \dfrac{y}{3}$ represents the sum of ____ and ____ .

$\dfrac{1}{4}$

201. Recall that $5\left(\dfrac{1}{7}\right)$ can be written $\left(\dfrac{5}{1}\right)\left(\dfrac{1}{7}\right)$, which is equal to $\dfrac{5}{7}$. Thus, $\dfrac{5}{7}$ can be written $5\left(\dfrac{1}{7}\right)$. $\dfrac{3}{4}$ can be written $3\left(\underline{}\right)$.

$\dfrac{1}{x+1}$

202. $\dfrac{3}{a}$ can be written $3\left(\dfrac{1}{a}\right)$ and $\dfrac{4}{x+1}$ can be written $4\left(\underline{}\right)$.

5

You first have
$(5)\dfrac{x}{5} = (5)2$
$x = 10.$

594. The equation $\dfrac{x}{3} = 4$ can be transformed to the equivalent equation $x = 12$ by multiplying each member by 3. $\dfrac{x}{5} = 2$ can be transformed to $x = 10$ by multiplying each member by_____ .

multiplying

595. $\dfrac{x}{7} = -4$ can be transformed to the equivalent equation $x = -28$ by_____ each member by 7.

$x = -12$

596. $\dfrac{x}{6} = -2$ can be transformed to the equivalent equation _____ = _____ by multiplying each member by 6.

equivalent; 3

597. $\dfrac{2}{3}x = 4$ can be transformed to the _____ equation $2x = 12$ by multiplying each member by____ .

6

If the solution is not evident by inspection, $2x = 12$ can be transformed to the equivalent equation $x = 6$ by dividing each member by 2.

598. The solution of $2x = 12$ is_____ .

$\dfrac{2}{3}x = 4$

599. Since $\dfrac{2}{3}x = 4$ and $2x = 12$ are equivalent, and 6 is the solution of $2x = 12$, 6 is also the solution of _____ = ____ .

5; 2

203. $\frac{2}{7} + \frac{3}{7}$ can be written $2\left(\frac{1}{7}\right) + 3\left(\frac{1}{7}\right)$. Similarly, $\frac{5}{6} + \frac{2}{6}$ can be written $\underline{\quad}\left(\frac{1}{6}\right) + \underline{\quad}\left(\frac{1}{6}\right)$.

$4x^2$; $6x^2$

204. $\frac{4x^2}{7} + \frac{6x^2}{7}$ can be written $\underline{\quad}\left(\frac{1}{7}\right) + \underline{\quad}\left(\frac{1}{7}\right)$.

x

205. Recall that one representation of the distributive law for integers says that if a, b, and c are integers, then

$$ba + ca = (b + c)a$$

where a has been factored from the expression $ab + ac$. Thus, $3x + 7x = (3 + 7)\underline{\quad}$ or $10x$.

$8 + 3$; $11y$

206. $8y + 3y = (\underline{\quad} + \underline{\quad})y = \underline{\quad}$.

7

207. By the distributive law,
$2\left(\frac{1}{3}\right) + 5\left(\frac{1}{3}\right) = (2 + 5)\frac{1}{3} = (\underline{\quad})\frac{1}{3}$.

$4 + 7$; 11

208. $4\left(\frac{1}{5}\right) + 7\left(\frac{1}{5}\right) = (\underline{\quad} + \underline{\quad})\frac{1}{5} = (\underline{\quad})\frac{1}{5}$.

$5 + 3$; 8

209. $5\left(\frac{1}{a}\right) + 3\left(\frac{1}{a}\right) = (\underline{\quad} + \underline{\quad})\frac{1}{a} = (\underline{\quad})\frac{1}{a}$.

$\frac{1}{10}$; $\frac{9}{10}$

210. $\frac{7}{10} + \frac{2}{10} = (7 + 2)\left(\underline{\quad}\right) = \underline{\quad}$.

$4 + 3$; $\frac{7}{9}$

211. $\frac{4}{9} + \frac{3}{9} = (\underline{\quad} + \underline{\quad})\frac{1}{9} = \underline{\quad}$.

-7

$\dfrac{a - 2b}{2a + b}$

$\dfrac{12ab + 2}{3ab - 3}$

589. Simplify $\dfrac{\frac{1}{4} + \frac{1}{3}}{\frac{1}{4} - \frac{1}{3}}$.

590. Simplify $\dfrac{\frac{1}{2b} - \frac{1}{a}}{\frac{1}{b} + \frac{1}{2a}}$.

591. Simplify $\dfrac{4 + \frac{2}{3ab}}{1 - \frac{1}{ab}}$.

Remark. A complex fraction is simply another way to express the quotient of two fractions. Thus, $\dfrac{a}{b} \div \dfrac{c}{d}$ and $\dfrac{a/b}{c/d}$ are two ways to express a quotient. Either expression may be used in place of the other and, in general, we use the form we find most convenient for whatever we happen to be doing at the moment.

We shall next direct our attention to the solution of some equations containing fractions. As usual, we shall solve these equations either by inspection, or by applying the addition, multiplication, or division axioms to generate equivalent equations until we arrive at an equation whose solution is obvious.

equivalent

592. Recall that equations having identical solutions are called equivalent equations. The solution of both $\dfrac{x}{3} = 4$ and $x = 12$ is 12. Therefore, the two equations are _____.

equivalent; 10

593. $\dfrac{x}{5} = 2$ and $x = 10$ are _____ equations because the solution to each equation is _____.

$\frac{1}{8}$

212. $\frac{a}{8} + \frac{b}{8} = a\left(\frac{1}{8}\right) + b\left(\frac{1}{8}\right)$, and, by the distributive

law, $a\left(\frac{1}{8}\right) + b\left(\frac{1}{8}\right) = (a + b)$ _____ .

$\frac{x + y}{4}$

213. $(a + b)\left(\frac{1}{8}\right) = \frac{a + b}{8}$. $(x + y)\left(\frac{1}{4}\right) = \dfrac{\rule{2cm}{0.4pt}}{4}$.

$\frac{1}{c}$

214. $\frac{a}{c} + \frac{b}{c} = (a + b)\left(\rule{1.5cm}{0.4pt}\right)$.

$\frac{a + b}{c}$

215. $(a + b)\left(\frac{1}{c}\right) = $ _____ .

$\frac{9}{11}$

216. Since $\frac{a}{c} + \frac{b}{c} = \frac{a + b}{c}$, the sum of two fractions having the same denominator can be written as a single fraction with a numerator equal to the sum of the two numerators and having the common denominator of the fractions. Thus, $\frac{1}{7} + \frac{5}{7} = \frac{6}{7}$ and

$\frac{8}{15} + \frac{3}{15} = \frac{11}{15}$. Similarly, $\frac{4}{11} + \frac{5}{11} = $ _____ .

$\frac{4}{5}$

217. $\frac{3}{5} + \frac{1}{5} = $ _____ .

$\frac{7}{a}$

218. $\frac{3}{a} + \frac{4}{a} = $ _____ .

$\frac{5}{x - 1}$

219. $\frac{2}{x - 1} + \frac{3}{x - 1} = $ _____ .

$\frac{a + 2}{a + b}$

220. $\frac{a}{a + b} + \frac{2}{a + b} = $ _____ .

$\dfrac{2b}{5a}$

582. $\dfrac{\dfrac{2}{5a^2b}(5a^2b^2)}{\dfrac{1}{ab^2}(5a^2b^2)} = \underline{\qquad}$.

18

583. The LCD of all fractions in the numerator and denominator of $\dfrac{\dfrac{1}{2} + \dfrac{1}{3}}{\dfrac{2}{9} + \dfrac{1}{6}}$ is $\underline{\qquad}$.

$\dfrac{15}{7}$

584. $\dfrac{\left(\dfrac{1}{2} + \dfrac{1}{3}\right)(18)}{\left(\dfrac{2}{9} + \dfrac{1}{6}\right)(18)} = \dfrac{\dfrac{1}{2}(18) + \dfrac{1}{3}(18)}{\dfrac{2}{9}(18) + \dfrac{1}{6}(18)} = \dfrac{9 + 6}{4 + 3} = \underline{\qquad}$.

$6a^2$

585. The LCD of all fractions in the numerator and denominator of $\dfrac{\dfrac{1}{a} + \dfrac{1}{2a}}{\dfrac{3}{a} - \dfrac{2}{3a^2}}$ is $\underline{\qquad}$.

$\dfrac{9a}{18a - 4}$

586. $\dfrac{\left(\dfrac{1}{a} + \dfrac{1}{2a}\right)(6a^2)}{\left(\dfrac{3}{a} - \dfrac{2}{3a^2}\right)(6a^2)} = \dfrac{\dfrac{1}{a}(6a^2) + \dfrac{1}{2a}(6a^2)}{\dfrac{3}{a}(6a^2) - \dfrac{2}{3a^2}(6a^2)} = \underline{\qquad}$.

2

587. Simplify $\dfrac{\dfrac{3}{4}}{\dfrac{3}{8}}$.

$\dfrac{3}{10a}$

588. Simplify $\dfrac{\dfrac{3b}{5a^3}}{\dfrac{2b}{a^2}}$.

$\dfrac{x^2 + x}{x - 1}$

$\dfrac{5a}{a - 1}$

$\dfrac{9a}{a + 1}$

$\dfrac{5x + 3}{4}$

$\dfrac{3x + 3}{5}$

$\dfrac{4x - 2}{x - 1}$

$\dfrac{4x}{x + 2}$

0

$\dfrac{1}{2}$

221. $\dfrac{x^2}{x - 1} + \dfrac{x}{x - 1} = $ _____ .

222. $\dfrac{3a}{a - 1} + \dfrac{2a}{a - 1} = \dfrac{3a + 2a}{a - 1}$. When like terms in the numerator are combined, the fraction can be written

_____ .

223. $\dfrac{6a}{a + 1} + \dfrac{3a}{a + 1} = $ _____ .

224. $\dfrac{2x + 1}{4} + \dfrac{3x + 2}{4} = \dfrac{2x + 1 + 3x + 2}{4}$. When like terms in the numerator are combined, the fraction can be written _____ .

225. $\dfrac{x - 1}{5} + \dfrac{2x + 4}{5} = $ _____ .

226. $\dfrac{x + 2}{x - 1} + \dfrac{3x - 4}{x - 1} = $ _____ .

227. $\dfrac{3x - 1}{x + 2} + \dfrac{x + 1}{x + 2} = $ _____ .

228. $\dfrac{x + 3}{x + 2} + \dfrac{-x - 3}{x + 2} = $ _____ .

229. It is customary always to represent sums of fractions in lowest terms. Thus, the sum of $\dfrac{3}{8}$ and $\dfrac{1}{8}$ is $\dfrac{4}{8}$ which, in lowest terms is _____ .

$\dfrac{5}{2}$

578. The fundamental principle of fractions can be applied to the complex fraction $\dfrac{\frac{1}{2}}{\frac{1}{5}}$, and the numerator and denominator can be multiplied by 10. $\dfrac{\frac{1}{2}(10)}{\frac{1}{5}(10)}$ produces the equal fraction _____ .

$15a^2b$

579. The LCD of the fraction in the numerator and the fraction in the denominator of $\dfrac{\frac{2}{3a}}{\frac{1}{5a^2b}}$ is _____ .

$\dfrac{10ab}{3}$

580. Multiplying the numerator and denominator of $\dfrac{\frac{2}{3a}}{\frac{1}{5a^2b}}$ by $15a^2b$ produces the equal fraction

$\dfrac{\frac{2}{3a}(15a^2b)}{\frac{1}{5a^2b}(15a^2b)}$ or _____ .

$5a^2b^2$

581. Many complex fractions can be changed to fractions that are not complex by applying the fundamental principle of fractions and multiplying numerator and denominator by the LCD of all fractions in the numerator and denominator. The LCD of the fractions in the numerator and denomina- tor of $\dfrac{\frac{2}{5a^2b}}{\frac{1}{ab^2}}$ is _____ .

$\dfrac{1}{2}$

$\dfrac{3}{4}$

$\dfrac{2}{3}$

$\dfrac{2a}{3}$

$\dfrac{1}{3a}$

$\dfrac{y}{x}$

$\dfrac{2a}{c}$

$-\dfrac{5}{9}$

sum

230. $\dfrac{1}{6} + \dfrac{2}{6} = \dfrac{3}{6} = $ _____ .

231. $\dfrac{5}{12} + \dfrac{1}{12} + \dfrac{3}{12} = \dfrac{9}{12} = $ _____ .

232. $\dfrac{4}{9} + \dfrac{1}{9} + \dfrac{1}{9} = $ _____ .

233. $\dfrac{4a}{9} + \dfrac{2a}{9} = \dfrac{6a}{9} = $ _____ .

234. $\dfrac{2}{15a} + \dfrac{3}{15a} = \dfrac{5}{15a} = $ _____ .

235. $\dfrac{3y}{10x} + \dfrac{7y}{10x} = \dfrac{10y}{10x} = $ _____ .

236. $\dfrac{2a}{7c} + \dfrac{a}{7c} + \dfrac{11a}{7c} = $ _____ .

237. Recall that the difference, $a - b$, of two integers a and b can be expressed as the sum $a + (-b)$. Similarly, the difference of two fractions, for example $\dfrac{7}{9} - \dfrac{5}{9}$, can be expressed as the sum $\dfrac{7}{9} + \left(\underline{\hspace{1.5cm}} \right)$.

238. $\dfrac{4}{5} - \dfrac{2}{5}$ represents the difference of $\dfrac{4}{5}$ and $\dfrac{2}{5}$ or the _____ of $\dfrac{4}{5}$ and $-\dfrac{2}{5}$.

$\dfrac{3}{2}$

You first have
$\dfrac{x + 1}{5} \div \dfrac{2x + 2}{15}$, then
$\dfrac{x + 1}{5} \cdot \dfrac{15}{2(x + 1)}$.

573. $\dfrac{\dfrac{x + 1}{5}}{\dfrac{2x + 2}{15}} = $ _____ .

$(x + 1)(x + 2)$

574. $\dfrac{\dfrac{x^2 - 4}{x + 1}}{\dfrac{x - 2}{(x + 1)^2}} = $ _____ .

Remark. There is another way to simplify complex fractions, a way that involves the fundamental principle of fractions. Before looking at this alternative approach, we shall first review the idea of the least common denominator (LCD) of a set of fractions.

12

575. Recall that the LCD of two or more fractions is the least number that can be divided exactly by the denominators of each of the fractions. The LCD of $\dfrac{1}{2}$ and $\dfrac{1}{3}$ is 6; the LCD of $\dfrac{1}{3}$ and $\dfrac{1}{4}$ is _____ .

$6a^2b^2$

576. The LCD of $\dfrac{1}{2a}$, $\dfrac{1}{3a^2b}$, and $\dfrac{1}{b^2}$ is _____ .

10

The fractions are $\dfrac{1}{2}$ and $\dfrac{1}{5}$.

577. The LCD of the fraction in the numerator and the fraction in the denominator of $\dfrac{\dfrac{1}{2}}{\dfrac{1}{5}}$ is _____ .

$\dfrac{8}{7}$; $-\dfrac{5}{7}$

239. $\dfrac{8}{7} - \dfrac{5}{7}$ represents the difference of $\dfrac{8}{7}$ and $\dfrac{5}{7}$ or the sum of _____ and _____.

$\dfrac{2}{5}$; $-\dfrac{1}{5}$

240. $\dfrac{2}{5} - \dfrac{1}{5}$ represents the sum of _____ and _____.

$\dfrac{-1}{5}$

241. Recall that in standard form $-\dfrac{3}{5}$ is written $\dfrac{-3}{5}$. In standard form, $-\dfrac{1}{5}$ is written _____.

$\dfrac{1}{5}$

242. Before writing $\dfrac{2}{5} - \dfrac{1}{5}$ as a single fraction, the second term may be written in standard form, and the result appears as $\dfrac{2}{5} + \dfrac{-1}{5}$. Since $2 + (-1) = 1$,

$\dfrac{2}{5} + \dfrac{-1}{5} =$ _____.

$\dfrac{1}{7}$

243. $\dfrac{4}{7} - \dfrac{3}{7} = \dfrac{4}{7} + \dfrac{-3}{7} = \dfrac{4 + (-3)}{7} =$ _____.

$\dfrac{5}{9}$

244. $\dfrac{7}{9} - \dfrac{2}{9} = \dfrac{7}{9} + \dfrac{-2}{9} =$ _____.

$\dfrac{3}{11}$

245. $\dfrac{5}{11} - \dfrac{2}{11} =$ _____.

$\dfrac{a - b}{7}$

246. $\dfrac{a}{7} - \dfrac{b}{7} =$ _____.

$\dfrac{-1}{y}$

247. $\dfrac{7}{2y} - \dfrac{9}{2y} = \dfrac{-2}{2y}$. This fraction can be reduced to lowest terms and written _____.

$\frac{3}{5}$

567. A complex fraction is a mathematical form expressing a quotient. $\dfrac{\dfrac{a}{b}}{\dfrac{c}{d}}$ is an alternative form for $\dfrac{a}{b} \div \dfrac{c}{d}$. Similarly,

$\dfrac{\dfrac{2}{3}}{\dfrac{3}{5}}$ is an alternative form for $\dfrac{2}{3} \div$ _____ .

$\dfrac{21}{20}$

568. $\dfrac{\dfrac{3}{5}}{\dfrac{4}{7}}$ equals $\dfrac{3}{5} \div \dfrac{4}{7}$. $\quad \dfrac{3}{5} \div \dfrac{4}{7} = \left(\dfrac{3}{5}\right)\left(\dfrac{7}{4}\right) =$ _____ .

$\dfrac{2}{3}$

569. $\dfrac{\dfrac{4}{9}}{\dfrac{2}{3}} = \dfrac{4}{9} \div \dfrac{2}{3} =$ _____ .

$\dfrac{3}{4}$

570. $\dfrac{\dfrac{3}{5}}{\dfrac{4}{5}} =$ _____ .

You first have $\dfrac{3}{5} \div \dfrac{4}{5}$, and then $\dfrac{3}{5} \cdot \dfrac{5}{4}$.

6

571. $\dfrac{\dfrac{4}{7}}{\dfrac{2}{21}} =$ _____ .

$\dfrac{2}{5}$

572. $\dfrac{\dfrac{x}{3}}{\dfrac{5x}{6}} =$ _____ .

$2a$

You first have $\frac{4a}{2}$, which reduces to $2a$.

248. $\dfrac{5a}{2} - \dfrac{a}{2} = $ _____ .

$\dfrac{-2x}{y}$

249. $\dfrac{3x}{4y} - \dfrac{11x}{4y} = $ _____ .

$\dfrac{9}{a}$

250. $\dfrac{4}{a} + \dfrac{7}{a} - \dfrac{2}{a} = $ _____ .

$\dfrac{2}{x+y}$

251. $\dfrac{5}{x+y} - \dfrac{2}{x+y} - \dfrac{1}{x+y} = $ _____ .

$\dfrac{a}{a+b}$

252. $\dfrac{3a}{a+b} - \dfrac{7a}{a+b} + \dfrac{5a}{a+b} = $ _____ .

$\dfrac{2x}{5}$

253. $\dfrac{x+1}{5} + \dfrac{x-1}{5} = \dfrac{x+1+x-1}{5} = $ _____ .

$\dfrac{3x+5}{3}$

254. $\dfrac{2x+7}{3} + \dfrac{x-2}{3} = $ _____ .

$\dfrac{10a-5b}{a}$

255. $\dfrac{3a-b}{a} + \dfrac{7a-4b}{a} = $ _____ .

$\dfrac{2x-4}{7}$

You first have $\dfrac{3x-x-4}{7}$

256. $\dfrac{3x}{7} - \dfrac{x+4}{7} = \dfrac{3x}{7} + \dfrac{-(x+4)}{7} = \dfrac{3x-(x+4)}{7} = $ _____ .

$\dfrac{12}{3}$

562. The quotient $6 \div 2$ can be written in the fractional form $\dfrac{6}{2}$. The quotient $12 \div 3$ can be written in the fractional form _____ .

$\dfrac{a}{b}$

563. The quotient $a \div b$ can be written in the fractional form _____ .

$\dfrac{\frac{2}{3}}{\frac{9}{4}}$

564. The quotient $\dfrac{2}{3} \div \dfrac{3}{5}$ can be written in the fractional form $\dfrac{\frac{2}{3}}{\frac{3}{5}}$. Similarly $\dfrac{2}{3} \div \dfrac{9}{4}$ can be written in the fractional form _____ .

complex

565. Any fraction that contains one or more fractions in its numerator or denominator is called a <u>complex</u> fraction. Thus, $\dfrac{\frac{2}{3}}{\frac{3}{5}}$ is a _____ fraction.

complex fraction

566. $\dfrac{2 + \frac{3}{x}}{x}$ is a _____ _____ .

$$\frac{3x + 8}{5}$$

257. $\dfrac{4x + 1}{5} - \dfrac{x - 7}{5} = \dfrac{4x + 1}{5} + \dfrac{-(x - 7)}{5} =$ _____.

$$\frac{a + 2b}{a}$$

258. $\dfrac{2a + b}{a} - \dfrac{a - b}{a} = \dfrac{2a + b}{a} + \dfrac{-(a - b)}{a} =$ _____.

$$\frac{-a - 2}{3}$$

259. $\dfrac{a - 1}{3} - \dfrac{2a + 1}{3} =$ _____.

You first have
$$\frac{a - 1}{3} + \frac{-(2a + 1)}{3}.$$

$$\frac{a + 5}{3y}$$

260. $\dfrac{2a + 1}{3y} - \dfrac{a - 4}{3y} =$ _____.

$$\frac{a + 2b}{3x}$$

261. $\dfrac{2a + 3b}{3x} - \dfrac{a + b}{3x} =$ _____.

$$\frac{2a}{3}$$

262. $\dfrac{a}{3} + \dfrac{2a + 1}{3} - \dfrac{a + 1}{3} =$ _____.

$$\frac{4}{3}$$

263. $\dfrac{a + 2b}{3a} + \dfrac{4a - b}{3a} - \dfrac{a + b}{3a} =$ _____.

Did you reduce the fraction?

$$\frac{2x - 3}{2x}$$

264. $\dfrac{3x - 1}{2x} - \dfrac{2x + 3}{2x} + \dfrac{x + 1}{2x} =$ _____.

$\dfrac{3(x + 1)}{4}$

555. $\dfrac{3x - 6}{4x + 4} \div \dfrac{x - 2}{(x + 1)^2} =$

$\dfrac{3(x - 2)}{4(x + 1)} \cdot \dfrac{(x + 1)^2}{(x - 2)} = \underline{\hspace{3cm}}.$

$\dfrac{6(3x + 1)}{2x + 1}$

556. $\dfrac{6x + 2}{x - 1} \div \dfrac{4x + 2}{6x - 6} = \underline{\hspace{3cm}}.$

$\dfrac{12}{x - 1}$

557. $\dfrac{3x + 6}{(x - 1)^2} \div \dfrac{x + 2}{4x - 4} = \underline{\hspace{3cm}}.$

$\dfrac{2(x + 1)}{(x - 3)}$

558. $\dfrac{x^2 + 2x + 1}{x - 3} \div \dfrac{x + 1}{2} =$

$\dfrac{(x + 1)(x + 1)}{(x - 3)} \cdot \dfrac{2}{(x + 1)} = \underline{\hspace{3cm}}.$

$x + 2$

559. $\dfrac{x^2 - 4}{x + 1} \div \dfrac{x - 2}{x + 1} =$

$\dfrac{(x - 2)(x + 2)}{(x + 1)} \cdot \dfrac{(x + 1)}{(x - 2)} = \underline{\hspace{2cm}}.$

$4x(x + 4)$

560. $\dfrac{x^2 + 5x + 4}{x} \div \dfrac{x + 1}{4x^2} = \underline{\hspace{3cm}}.$

$2(x - 3)$

561. $\dfrac{x^2 - 9}{2x + 1} \div \dfrac{x + 3}{4x + 2} = \underline{\hspace{3cm}}.$

Remark. You have found that the division of algebraic fractions involves nothing new; you simply "invert the divisor and multiply." Of course, in working with algebraic fractions, you also have some factoring to do, but this does not alter the division process.

We are now going to turn our attention to a different way of denoting the division of one fraction by another.

Remark. The addition of fractions with the same denominator is simply a matter of adding the numerators of the fractions. What about the addition of fractions with different denominators? We shall begin by reviewing the addition of arithmetic fractions.

common denominator

265. To add fractions that do not have a common denominator, it is necessary to change one or both fractions to equal fractions that have a common denominator. Thus, $\frac{1}{2} + \frac{1}{4}$ cannot be written as a single fraction until the fractions have a _____ _____ .

4

266. To find a common denominator for two or more fractions with unlike denominators, it is necessary to find a number that is a multiple of each of the denominators. For instance, a common denominator for the fractions $\frac{3}{8}$ and $\frac{1}{4}$ is 8, because 8 is an integral multiple of both 8 and ____ .

3; 6

Or 6; 3.

267. A common denominator for the two fractions $\frac{1}{3}$ and $\frac{1}{6}$ is 12 because 12 is an integral multiple of both 3 and 6. However, 6 is also a common denominator of $\frac{1}{3}$ and $\frac{1}{6}$ because 6 is a multiple of both _____ and ____ .

least common denominator

268. The smallest positive integer that is an integral multiple of the denominators of a group of fractions is called the least common denominator (LCD). Because 10 is the smallest positive integer that is an integral multiple of 2 and 5, 10 is the _____ _____ _____ of the fractions $\frac{1}{2}$ and $\frac{3}{5}$.

least common denominator

269. Because 12 is the smallest positive integer that is an integral multiple of 3 and 12, 12 is the _____ _____ _____ of the fractions $\frac{1}{3}$ and $\frac{5}{12}$.

$\dfrac{3}{(x + 3)(x - 1)}$

550. $\dfrac{x - 1}{x + 3} \div \dfrac{(x - 1)^2}{3} =$ _____ .

$\dfrac{(2x - 1)(x + 1)}{(x + 3)}$

551. $\dfrac{3(2x - 1)}{x + 1} \div \dfrac{3(x + 3)}{(x + 1)^2} =$ _____ .

Remark. As you have observed, the numerators and denominators of the fractions we have been dividing have been given in factored form. However, such fractions usually appear with numerators and denominators in unfactored form. These are what we shall consider in the next sequence of frames.

$\dfrac{4}{x}$

552. Before attempting to simplify a quotient, all numerators and denominators of the fractions involved should be written in completely factored form. Thus, $\dfrac{x^2 - x}{2} \div \dfrac{x^3 - x^2}{8}$ should first be written $\dfrac{x(x - 1)}{2} \div \dfrac{x^2(x - 1)}{8}$, and then as $\dfrac{x(x - 1)}{2} \cdot \dfrac{8}{x^2(x - 1)}$, which reduces to _____ .

$\dfrac{9}{2}$

553. To simplify the quotient $\dfrac{3x - 6}{2x + 4} \div \dfrac{x - 2}{3x + 6}$, we first write $\dfrac{3(x - 2)}{2(x + 2)} \div \dfrac{(x - 2)}{3(x + 2)}$. Then, inverting the divisor, we have $\dfrac{3(x - 2)}{2(x + 2)} \cdot \dfrac{3(x + 2)}{(x - 2)}$, which reduces to _____ .

4

554. $\dfrac{2x + 2}{3} \div \dfrac{x + 1}{6} = \dfrac{2(x + 1)}{3} \cdot \dfrac{6}{(x + 1)} =$ _____ .

LCD	**270.** "Least common denominator" is usually abbreviated LCD. Because 15 is the smallest positive integer that is an integral multiple of 3 and 5, 15 is the _____ of $\frac{1}{3}$ and $\frac{3}{5}$.
LCD	**271.** Because 30 is the smallest positive integer that is an integral multiple of 2, 3, and 5, 30 is the _____ of $\frac{1}{2}$, $\frac{2}{3}$, and $\frac{4}{5}$.
8	**272.** The LCD of the fractions $\frac{3}{8}$ and $\frac{1}{2}$ is ____.
2·5	**273.** To find the LCD of a set of fractions, it is usually easiest first to express each denominator in completely factored form. The completely factored form of 6 is 2·3. The completely factored form of 10 is _____.
3·5	**274.** The completely factored form of 15 is _____.
2·3·3	**275.** The completely factored form of 12 is 2·2·3. The completely factored form of 18 is _____.
2·3; 3·5	**276.** The completely factored form of 6 is _____ and the completely factored form of 15 is _____.
30	**277.** To find the LCD of the fractions $\frac{1}{6}$ and $\frac{1}{15}$, the denominators 6 and 15 are first completely factored as 2·3 and 3·5, respectively. Since any common multiple must contain all of the factors of both 6 and 15, it must contain the factors 2, 3, and 5. Thus, the LCD of of $\frac{1}{6}$ and $\frac{4}{15}$ is (2)(3)(5) or ____.

$$\frac{ad}{bc}$$

541. $\frac{a}{b} \div \frac{c}{d} = \left(\frac{a}{b}\right)\left(\frac{d}{c}\right) = \underline{\hspace{2cm}}$.

$$\frac{15x}{8y}$$

542. $\frac{3x}{4} \div \frac{2y}{5} = \left(\frac{3x}{4}\right)\left(\frac{5}{2y}\right) = \underline{\hspace{2cm}}$.

$$\frac{2}{x}$$

543. $\frac{2y}{3} \div \frac{x}{2} = \left(\frac{2y}{3}\right)\left(\underline{\hspace{1cm}}\right) = \frac{4y}{3x}$.

$$\frac{6y}{5x}$$

544. $\frac{3y}{5} \div \frac{x}{2} = \underline{\hspace{2cm}}$.

$$\frac{x}{y}$$

545. $\frac{x^3}{y^2} \div \frac{x^2}{y} = \left(\frac{x^3}{y^2}\right)\left(\frac{y}{x^2}\right) = \underline{\hspace{2cm}}$.

$$\frac{x^2 z}{y}$$

546. $\frac{x^3 y}{z} \div \frac{xy^2}{z^2} = \underline{\hspace{2cm}}$.

$$\frac{5x^3 y^2}{2}$$

547. $\frac{2x^4 y}{5} \div \frac{4x}{25y} = \underline{\hspace{2cm}}$.

$$\frac{4}{3x}$$

548. $\frac{x + 1}{3} \div \frac{3x}{4} = \left(\frac{x + 1}{3}\right)\underline{\hspace{1.5cm}} = \frac{4(x + 1)}{9x}$.

$$\frac{8(x + 2)}{5}$$

549. $\frac{2(x + 1)(x + 2)}{5} \div \frac{(x + 1)}{4} =$

You could have $\frac{8x + 16}{5}$,
but we will leave answers
in factored form from
now on.

$\frac{2(x + 1)(x + 2)}{5} \cdot \frac{(4)}{(x + 1)} = \underline{\hspace{2cm}}$.

2·3; 3·7

278. The LCD of the fractions $\frac{1}{6}$ and $\frac{1}{21}$ can be found by first factoring 6 as_____and 21 as_____.

6; 21

279. The LCD of the fractions $\frac{1}{6}$ and $\frac{1}{21}$ is 2·3·7 or 42, since 42 contains all the factors of____and____.

three

280. Each factor in the LCD of a group of fractions must occur the greatest number of times it occurs in any one of the denominators. Since the completely factored form of 8 and 12 are respectively 2·2·2 and 2·2·3, the factor 2 must occur *three* times in the LCD of the fractions $\frac{1}{8}$ and $\frac{1}{12}$, because the factor 2 occurs_____times in 8.

2·2; 2·5

281. The LCD of the fractions $\frac{1}{4}$ and $\frac{3}{10}$ can be found by first factoring 4 as_____and 10 as_____.

4; 10

282. The LCD of the fractions $\frac{1}{4}$ and $\frac{3}{10}$ is 2·2·5 or 20, since 20 contains all the factors of_____and____.

24

Or 2·2·2·3.

283. Since the factors of 6 are 3 and 2, and the factors of 8 are 2, 2, and 2, the LCD of $\frac{5}{6}$ and $\frac{3}{8}$ is____.

24

284. The LCD of $\frac{2}{3}, \frac{5}{6}$, and $\frac{7}{8}$ is____.

30

Or 2·3·5.

285. The LCD of $\frac{1}{6}, \frac{1}{2}$, and $\frac{4}{15}$ is____.

$\dfrac{2}{3}$

534. To write the quotient $\dfrac{a}{b} \div \dfrac{c}{d}$ as an equal product $\left(\dfrac{a}{b}\right)\left(\dfrac{d}{c}\right)$ is frequently stated "invert the divisor and multiply." Thus, $\dfrac{4}{5} \div \dfrac{3}{2} = \left(\dfrac{4}{5}\right)\left(\dfrac{2}{3}\right)$ and $\dfrac{6}{7} \div \dfrac{3}{2} = \dfrac{6}{7}\left(\underline{}\right)$.

$\left(\dfrac{3}{5}\right)\left(\dfrac{6}{5}\right)$

535. $\dfrac{3}{5} \div \dfrac{5}{6} = \left(\underline{}\right)\left(\underline{}\right)$.

$\dfrac{18}{25}$

536. $\left(\dfrac{3}{5}\right)\left(\dfrac{6}{5}\right) = \underline{}$.

$\dfrac{8}{7}$

537. $\dfrac{4}{7} \div \dfrac{1}{2} = \left(\dfrac{4}{7}\right)\left(\dfrac{2}{1}\right) = \underline{}$.

$\left(\dfrac{3}{2}\right)\left(\dfrac{5}{2}\right)$

538. $\dfrac{3}{2} \div \dfrac{2}{5} = \left(\underline{}\right)\left(\underline{}\right)$.

$\dfrac{7}{6}$

539. $\dfrac{7}{8} \div \dfrac{3}{4} = \underline{}$.

You first have $\left(\dfrac{7}{8}\right)\left(\dfrac{4}{3}\right)$.

$\dfrac{12}{25}$

540. $\dfrac{12}{15} \div \dfrac{5}{3} = \underline{}$.

Remark. We shall now begin working with fractions containing variables. The few division problems in the preceding frames should serve to review the notion of "invert the divisor and multiply."

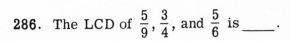

36

286. The LCD of $\frac{5}{9}$, $\frac{3}{4}$, and $\frac{5}{6}$ is _____ .

$\frac{3}{3}$

287. Recall the fundamental principle of fractions

$$\frac{a}{b} = \frac{ac}{bc}.$$

This relationship states that the result of multiplying the numerator and denominator of a fraction by the same nonzero number is an equal fraction. Thus, $\frac{3}{4}$ =

$\frac{3}{4}\left(\underline{} \right) = \frac{9}{12}.$

$\frac{8}{14}$

288. $\frac{4}{7} = \frac{4(2)}{7(2)} = $ _____ .

$\frac{6}{6}$

289. $\frac{4}{5}\left(\underline{} \right) = \frac{24}{30}$

building factor

290. Recall that the number by which both numerator and denominator are multiplied in building a fraction to an equal fraction in higher terms is called the building factor. Thus, to change $\frac{3}{7}$ to $\frac{9}{21}$, the numerator and denominator of $\frac{3}{7}$ are multiplied by the

_____ _____ , 3.

6

291. To obtain a building factor that will change $\frac{3}{4}$ to an equal fraction, $\frac{?}{24}$, you ask "By what number must 4 be multiplied to yield 24?" Since the answer is 6, the desired building factor is_____.

$\frac{18}{24}$

292. $\frac{3}{4} = \frac{3(6)}{4(6)} = $ _____ .

$\frac{1}{4}$

530. The quotient $\frac{1}{4} \div \frac{5}{7}$ is the number q such that

$$\frac{5}{7} \cdot q = \underline{\qquad} .$$

$\left(\frac{1}{4}\right)\left(\frac{7}{5}\right)$

Or $\frac{7}{20}$.

531. To find the quotient q so that $\frac{5}{7}(q) = \frac{1}{4}$, each

member of the equation can be multiplied by $\frac{7}{5}$ to yield

$\left(\frac{7}{5}\right)\left(\frac{5}{7}\right)(q) = \left(\frac{1}{4}\right)\left(\frac{7}{5}\right)$, from which q equals the product

$\left(\frac{1}{4}\right)\left(\frac{7}{5}\right)$. The quotient $\frac{1}{4} \div \frac{5}{7}$ equals the product $\underline{\qquad}$.

Remark. Is this clear to you? What is happening is this: We are look-
ing for a quotient $q = \frac{1}{4} \div \frac{5}{7}$. To find the quotient, we use the fact that the
quotient must multiply the divisor, $\frac{5}{7}$, to yield the dividend, $\frac{1}{4}$. That is, $\frac{5}{7}$
times q, must be equal to $\frac{1}{4}$. In symbols this is given by $\frac{5}{7} \cdot q = \frac{1}{4}$. Then,
to find the quotient, q, we just solve this equation for q. This gives us
$q = \frac{1}{4} \cdot \frac{7}{5}$. Thus $\frac{1}{4} \div \frac{5}{7} = \frac{1}{4} \cdot \frac{7}{5}$. In the following frames, this argument is
repeated for the quotient of any two fractions.

$\frac{a}{b}$

532. The quotient $\frac{a}{b} \div \frac{c}{d}$, where b, c, and d do not

equal 0, is a number q such that $\frac{c}{d}(q) = \underline{\qquad} .$

$\frac{ad}{bc}$

533. To find q so that $\frac{c}{d}(q) = \frac{a}{b}$, each member of the

equation can be multiplied by $\frac{d}{c}$ to yield

$\left(\frac{d}{c}\right)\left(\frac{c}{d}\right)(q) = \left(\frac{a}{b}\right)\left(\frac{d}{c}\right)$, from which $q = \left(\frac{a}{b}\right)\left(\frac{d}{c}\right)$.

Thus, the quotient $q = \frac{a}{b} \div \frac{c}{d}$ or the product $\underline{\qquad}$.

4

293. 7 must be multiplied by 4 to yield 28. Therefore, the building factor necessary to change $\frac{3}{7}$ to an equal fraction $\frac{?}{28}$ is____.

$\frac{12}{28}$

294. $\frac{3}{7} = \frac{3(4)}{7(4)} =$ ____.

4

295. The LCD of $\frac{1}{2}$ and $\frac{1}{4}$ is____.

4

296. The sum $\frac{1}{2} + \frac{1}{4}$ can be written as an equal sum $\frac{1(2)}{2(2)} + \frac{1}{4}$ in which both fractions have a common denominator,___.

$\frac{3}{4}$

297. $\frac{2}{4} + \frac{1}{4} =$ ____.

8

298. The LCD of $\frac{1}{2}$ and $\frac{1}{8}$ is____.

$\frac{5}{8}$

299. The sum $\frac{1}{2} + \frac{1}{8}$ can be written as an equal sum $\frac{1(4)}{2(4)} + \frac{1}{8}$. These fractions have the common denominator 8 and can be combined to give ____.

$\frac{7}{9}$

300. $\frac{1}{3} + \frac{4}{9} = \frac{1(3)}{3(3)} + \frac{4}{9} =$ ____.

$\dfrac{y(y-1)}{(y+4)}$

524. $\dfrac{y^2-1}{y^2-16} \cdot \dfrac{y^2-4y}{y+1} =$

$\dfrac{(y-1)(y+1)}{(y-4)(y+4)} \cdot \dfrac{y(y-4)}{(y+1)} = $ _____ .

$\dfrac{4x}{x-3}$

525. $\dfrac{x^2+x-6}{2x^2+6x} \cdot \dfrac{8x^2}{x^2-5x+6} = $ _____ .

Remark. Closely allied with products are quotients. Our next task is to examine the process of division as it relates to fractions, and, in particular, to justify the familiar rule used when dividing fractions, "invert the divisor and multiply."

6

526. Recall that the quotient of two numbers $\dfrac{a}{b}$ where b does not equal zero is defined to be the number c such that bc equals a. For example, $\dfrac{12}{3} = 4$ because $(3)(4) = 12$ and $\dfrac{6}{2} = 3$ because $(2)(3) = $ _____ .

(2)(8)

Or (8)(2).

527. $\dfrac{16}{8} = 2$ because (____)(____) = 16.

$-12; \quad (2)(-12)$

528. $\dfrac{-24}{2} = $ _____ because (____)(____) = -24.

$\dfrac{2}{3}$

This is the dividend.

529. The quotient of two fractions, say $\dfrac{2}{3} \div \dfrac{5}{7}$, is defined to be the number q such that the divisor, $\dfrac{5}{7}$, times the quotient, q, equals the dividend, $\dfrac{2}{3}$. That is,

$\dfrac{5}{7} \cdot q = $ _____ .

24

$\dfrac{17}{24}$

6

$\dfrac{7}{6}$

10

$\dfrac{11}{10}$

$\dfrac{(5)1}{(5)2} + \dfrac{(2)3}{(2)5}$.

$\dfrac{17}{12}$

301. To write $\dfrac{1}{3} + \dfrac{3}{8}$ as a single fraction, it is first necessary to find a common denominator for the fractions. The LCD of $\dfrac{1}{3}$ and $\dfrac{3}{8}$ is____ .

302. $\dfrac{1}{3} + \dfrac{3}{8}$ can be written as the equal sum $\dfrac{(8)1}{(8)3} + \dfrac{(3)3}{(3)8}$. These fractions have a common denominator, 24, and may be combined to give _____ .

303. The LCD of $\dfrac{1}{2}$ and $\dfrac{2}{3}$ is___ .

304. $\dfrac{2}{3} + \dfrac{1}{2}$ can be written as the equal sum $\dfrac{(2)2}{(2)3} + \dfrac{(3)1}{(3)2}$. These fractions can be combined and written as _____ .

305. The LCD of the fractions in $\dfrac{1}{2} + \dfrac{3}{5}$ is_____ .

306. The sum $\dfrac{1}{2} + \dfrac{3}{5}$ can be written as the single fraction _____ .

307. The sum $\dfrac{2}{3} + \dfrac{3}{4}$ can be written as the single fraction _____ .

$\dfrac{2}{5}$

517. $\dfrac{2}{x+3} \cdot \dfrac{x+3}{5} = \dfrac{2(x+3)}{5(x+3)} =$ _____ .

$\dfrac{3}{4}$

518. Polynomials should be written in factored form before seeking factors that are common to a numerator and a denominator. Thus, $\dfrac{5}{2x+2} \cdot \dfrac{3x+3}{10} =$

$\dfrac{5}{2(x+1)} \cdot \dfrac{3(x+1)}{2 \cdot 5} = \dfrac{3(5)(x+1)}{2 \cdot 2(5)(x+1)} =$ _____ .

$\dfrac{5}{2}$

519. $\dfrac{5a+25}{2a} \cdot \dfrac{a}{a+5} =$ _____ .

You first have
$\dfrac{5(a+5)}{2a} \cdot \dfrac{a}{(a+5)}$.

-1

520. $\dfrac{-3}{a-3} \cdot \dfrac{2a-6}{6} =$ _____ .

$\dfrac{4}{15}$

521. $\dfrac{2a+8}{5a} \cdot \dfrac{2a}{3a+12} = \dfrac{2(a+4)}{5a} \cdot \dfrac{2a}{3(a+4)} =$ _____ .

$\dfrac{1}{8}$

522. $\dfrac{x-1}{2x+6} \cdot \dfrac{x+3}{4x-4} =$ _____ .

$3(x+1)$

523. $\dfrac{x^2-2x-3}{x+3} \cdot \dfrac{3x+9}{x-3} =$

$\dfrac{(x-3)(x+1)}{(x+3)} \cdot \dfrac{3(x+3)}{(x-3)} =$ _____ .

15

308. The difference $\frac{1}{3} - \frac{2}{5}$ can be written as the sum $\frac{1}{3} + \frac{-2}{5}$. The LCD of $\frac{1}{3}$ and $\frac{-2}{5}$ is _____.

$\frac{-1}{15}$

309. The sum $\frac{1}{3} + \frac{-2}{5}$ can be written as the equal sum $\frac{(5)1}{(5)3} + \frac{(3)(-2)}{(3)\ 5}$ or $\frac{5}{15} + \frac{-6}{15}$. This sum can be combined into the single fraction _____.

12

310. The difference $\frac{3}{4} - \frac{2}{3}$ can be written as the sum $\frac{3}{4} + \frac{-2}{3}$. The LCD of $\frac{3}{4}$ and $\frac{-2}{3}$ is _____.

$\frac{1}{12}$

311. $\frac{3}{4} + \frac{-2}{3}$ can be written as the single fraction _____.

$\frac{-1}{6}$

312. $\frac{1}{2} - \frac{2}{3}$ can be written as the single fraction _____.

$\frac{1}{2}$

313. The word "simplify," as it pertains to the sum or difference of two fractions, means to write the sum or difference as a single fraction in lowest terms. Thus $\frac{7}{10} - \frac{1}{5}$ can be simplified and written as the single fraction _____.

Remark. You should now be able to simplify the sum of any number of arithmetic fractions, both fractions with common denominators, and fractions with unlike denominators. The principles applied to arithmetic fractions are equally applicable to algebraic fractions. In the work that follows, you are going to encounter a lot of symbolism

511. If any of the fractions in a product involve negative signs, the fractions are first written in standard form, and then the reduction of the product is completed. For example, $\left(-\dfrac{6}{-5}\right)\left(-\dfrac{2}{3}\right)$ would

first be written $\left(\dfrac{6}{5}\right)\left(\dfrac{-2}{3}\right)$, and then $\dfrac{\overset{2}{\cancel{6}}}{5}\left(\dfrac{-2}{\underset{1}{\cancel{3}}}\right) = \dfrac{-4}{5}$.

Similarly, $\left(\dfrac{-8}{-3}\right)\left(-\dfrac{3}{4}\right) = \left(\dfrac{8}{3}\right)\left(\dfrac{-3}{4}\right) =$ _____ .

$\dfrac{6}{5}$

512. $\left(\dfrac{-4}{5}\right)\left(\dfrac{3}{-2}\right) =$ _____ .

You first have $\left(\dfrac{-4}{5}\right)\left(\dfrac{-3}{2}\right)$.

$\dfrac{x}{6}$

513. $\left(\dfrac{-3x^2}{4}\right)\left(-\dfrac{2}{9x}\right) =$ _____ .

$\dfrac{-3x^2}{2y}$

514. $\dfrac{-6xy}{7} \cdot \dfrac{14x}{8y^2} =$ _____ .

$\dfrac{a^2c}{4}$

515. $\left(\dfrac{-5ab}{6c}\right)\left(\dfrac{-3ac^2}{10b}\right) =$ _____ .

$\dfrac{x+2}{x-4} ; \dfrac{x+2}{x-4}$

Parentheses are not necessary in the final result.

516. When binomial factors are involved in a product, it is best to insert parentheses around the binomials if the parentheses are not already present. Thus, $\dfrac{x-3}{x-4} \cdot \dfrac{x+2}{x-3}$ should first be written $\dfrac{(x-3)}{(x-4)} \cdot \dfrac{(x+2)}{(x-3)}$,

and then reduced either as $\dfrac{(x+2)}{(x-4)} \cdot \dfrac{(x-3)}{(x-3)} =$

_____ , or as $\dfrac{\cancel{(x-3)}}{(x-4)} \cdot \dfrac{(x+2)}{\underset{1}{\cancel{(x-3)}}} =$ _____ .

that may look somewhat complicated. Be sure you read each frame carefully, and make sure that the meaning of the symbolism is clear to you at every step.

9

314. The LCD of the fractions $\frac{x}{3} + \frac{2x}{9}$ is ____ .

$\frac{5x}{9}$

315. The sum $\frac{x}{3} + \frac{2x}{9}$ is equal to the sum $\frac{(3)x}{(3)3} + \frac{2x}{9}$, which can be written as the single fraction ____ .

8

316. The LCD of the fractions in $\frac{5x}{8} - \frac{x}{2}$ is ____ .

$\frac{x}{8}$

317. The difference $\frac{5x}{8} - \frac{x}{2}$ can be written as the single fraction ____ .

$\frac{5x}{8} - \frac{(4)x}{(4)2}$.

20

318. The LCD of the fractions in $\frac{ab}{20} + \frac{ab}{10}$ is ____ .

$\frac{3ab}{20}$

319. $\frac{ab}{20} + \frac{ab}{10} = \frac{ab}{20} + \frac{ab(2)}{10(2)} =$ ____ .

6

320. The LCD of the fractions in $\frac{xy}{3} + \frac{5xy}{6}$ is ____ .

$\frac{7xy}{6}$

321. $\frac{xy}{3} + \frac{5xy}{6} =$ ____ .

$\dfrac{2}{27}$

502. $\dfrac{8}{9} \cdot \dfrac{1}{12} = \dfrac{2 \cdot 2 \cdot 2}{3 \cdot 3 \cdot 2 \cdot 2 \cdot 3} = \dfrac{2(2 \cdot 2)}{3 \cdot 3 \cdot 3(2 \cdot 2)} = \underline{\hspace{2cm}}.$

$\dfrac{2}{27}$

503. $\dfrac{8}{9} \cdot \dfrac{1}{12} = \dfrac{\overset{2}{\cancel{8}}}{9} \cdot \dfrac{1}{\underset{3}{\cancel{12}}} = \underline{\hspace{2cm}}.$

$\dfrac{3}{5}$

504. $\dfrac{2}{3} \cdot \dfrac{9}{10} = \dfrac{2 \cdot 3 \cdot 3}{3 \cdot 2 \cdot 5} = \dfrac{3(2 \cdot 3)}{5(2 \cdot 3)} = \underline{\hspace{2cm}}.$

$\dfrac{3}{5}$

505. $\dfrac{2}{3} \cdot \dfrac{9}{10} = \dfrac{\overset{1}{\cancel{2}}}{\underset{1}{\cancel{3}}} \cdot \dfrac{\overset{3}{\cancel{9}}}{\underset{5}{\cancel{10}}} = \underline{\hspace{2cm}}.$

$\dfrac{4x^2}{5}$

506. $\dfrac{6x^3}{5} \cdot \dfrac{2}{3x} = \dfrac{2 \cdot 3xxx \cdot 2}{5 \cdot 3 \cdot x} = \dfrac{2 \cdot 2xx(3x)}{5(3x)} = \underline{\hspace{2cm}}.$

$\dfrac{7}{3a^2}$

507. $\dfrac{7a}{3} \cdot \dfrac{1}{a^3} = \dfrac{7a}{3aaa} = \dfrac{7(a)}{3aa(a)} = \underline{\hspace{2cm}}.$

$\dfrac{3x}{2}$

508. $\dfrac{2}{3x} \cdot \dfrac{9x^2}{4} = \underline{\hspace{2cm}}.$

$4y$

509. $6x^2y \cdot \dfrac{2}{3x^2} = \dfrac{6x^2y}{1} \cdot \dfrac{2}{3x^2} = \underline{\hspace{2cm}}.$

$\dfrac{5}{xy}$

510. $\dfrac{1}{x^3y^3} \cdot 5x^2y^2 = \dfrac{1}{x^3y^3} \cdot \dfrac{5x^2y^2}{1} = \underline{\hspace{2cm}}.$

8

322. The LCD of the fractions in $\dfrac{3a}{8} - \dfrac{a}{4}$ is _____ .

$\dfrac{a}{8}$

323. $\dfrac{3a}{8} - \dfrac{a}{4} = \dfrac{3a}{8} + \dfrac{-a\,(2)}{4\,(2)} =$ _____ .

12

324. The LCD of the fractions in $\dfrac{ab}{12} - \dfrac{ab}{2}$ is _____ .

$\dfrac{-5ab}{12}$

325. $\dfrac{ab}{12} - \dfrac{ab}{2} =$ _____ .

8

326. The LCD of $\dfrac{1}{2}, \dfrac{1}{4},$ and $\dfrac{1}{8}$ is _____ .

$\dfrac{7}{8}$

327. $\dfrac{1}{2} + \dfrac{1}{4} + \dfrac{1}{8} = \dfrac{1\,(4)}{2\,(4)} + \dfrac{1\,(2)}{4\,(2)} + \dfrac{1}{8} =$ _____ .

12

328. The LCD of $\dfrac{2a}{3}, \dfrac{3a}{4},$ and $\dfrac{5a}{12}$ is _____ .

$\dfrac{a}{3}$

329. $\dfrac{2a}{3} - \dfrac{3a}{4} + \dfrac{5a}{12} = \dfrac{2a\,(4)}{3\,(4)} + \dfrac{-3a\,(3)}{4\,(3)} + \dfrac{5a}{12} =$ _____ .

You first have $\dfrac{4a}{12}$.

$\dfrac{-5x}{9}$

330. $\dfrac{x}{18} + \dfrac{2x}{9} - \dfrac{5x}{6} =$ _____ .

$\dfrac{2x^2}{3y} ; \dfrac{2x^2}{3y}$

498. $\dfrac{6x^3y}{9xy^2} = \dfrac{2x^2 \cdot 3xy}{3y \cdot 3xy} = $ _____ , or by an

alternative form $\dfrac{\dfrac{2x^2}{\cancel{6x^3}}}{\dfrac{\cancel{9xy^2}}{3y}} = $ _____ , where $6x^3y$ and

$9xy^2$ have each been divided by $3xy$.

$\dfrac{3}{10} ; \dfrac{3}{10}$

499. To multiply fractions that contain common factors in numerators and denominators, for example $\dfrac{3}{4} \cdot \dfrac{2}{5}$, we can represent the product in completely factored form and then apply the fundamental principle of fractions to write an equal fraction without the common factors. Thus,
$\dfrac{3}{4} \cdot \dfrac{2}{5} = \dfrac{3 \cdot 2}{4 \cdot 5} = \dfrac{(3)(2)}{(2 \cdot 5)(2)} = \dfrac{3}{2 \cdot 5} = $ _____ . The alternative form (slant bar) can also be used to indicate the division of common factors from numerators and denominators. Thus,

$\dfrac{3}{\overset{}{\underset{2}{\cancel{4}}}} \cdot \dfrac{\overset{1}{\cancel{2}}}{5} = \dfrac{3 \cdot 1}{2 \cdot 5} = $ _____ .

Remark. The preceding frames are largely review of earlier material in this unit. However, it is important that you be able to simplify fractional expressions by dividing out common factors. You should understand that the two methods explained are equivalent, and that either may be used when desired.

$\dfrac{1}{18}$

500. $\dfrac{3}{8} \cdot \dfrac{4}{27} = \dfrac{3 \cdot 2 \cdot 2}{2 \cdot 2 \cdot 2 \cdot 3 \cdot 3 \cdot 3} =$

$\dfrac{1(2 \cdot 2 \cdot 3)}{2 \cdot 3 \cdot 3(2 \cdot 2 \cdot 3)} = $ _____ .

$\dfrac{1}{18}$

501. $\dfrac{3}{8} \cdot \dfrac{12}{27} = \dfrac{\overset{1}{\cancel{3}}}{\underset{2}{\cancel{8}}} \cdot \dfrac{\overset{1}{\cancel{4}}}{\underset{9}{27}} = $ _____ .

$\dfrac{5a - 1}{4}$

You first have
$\dfrac{a + 1 + 4a - 2}{4}$.

331. The expression $\dfrac{a + 1}{4} + \dfrac{2a - 1}{2}$ equals $\dfrac{(a + 1)}{4} + \dfrac{(2)}{(2)}\dfrac{(2a - 1)}{2}$, which can be written as the single fraction $\dfrac{a + 1 + 2(2a - 1)}{4}$. This single fraction can be simplified to _____ .

6

332. The LCD of the fractions in $\dfrac{a - 3}{3} + \dfrac{2a - 1}{6}$ is _____ .

$\dfrac{4a - 7}{6}$

You first have
$\dfrac{2(a - 3) + 2a - 1}{6}$.

333. $\dfrac{a - 3}{3} + \dfrac{2a - 1}{6}$ can be written as the single fraction _____ .

$\dfrac{11a - 22}{10}$

334. Write $\dfrac{a - 4}{2} + \dfrac{3a - 1}{5}$ as a single fraction.

12

335. The LCD of the fractions in $\dfrac{a - 1}{2} + \dfrac{3a + 1}{3} + \dfrac{a - 4}{4}$ is _____ .

$\dfrac{21a - 14}{12}$

336. Simplify $\dfrac{a - 1}{2} + \dfrac{3a + 1}{3} + \dfrac{a - 4}{4}$.
(Write as a single fraction in lowest terms.)

4

337. The LCD of the fractions in $\dfrac{a + 1}{4} - \dfrac{2a - 1}{2}$ is _____ .

$\dfrac{6x^2}{y^2}$

$\dfrac{12x^5}{y}$

$\dfrac{6x^3}{y}$

$\dfrac{8a^4}{75}$

$\dfrac{2x^4}{3y^4}$

$\dfrac{4}{5}$

2

491. $\dfrac{2x^2}{y} \cdot \dfrac{3}{y} =$ _____ .

492. $3x^2 \cdot \dfrac{4x^3}{y} = \dfrac{3x^2}{1} \cdot \dfrac{4x^3}{y} =$ _____ .

493. $\dfrac{2x^2}{y} \cdot 3x =$ _____ .

494. $\dfrac{a}{3} \cdot \dfrac{2a}{5} \cdot \dfrac{4a^2}{5} =$ _____ .

495. $\dfrac{x^2}{y} \cdot \dfrac{2x}{y^2} \cdot \dfrac{x}{3y} =$ _____ .

496. Recall that $\dfrac{4}{6} = \dfrac{2 \cdot 2}{3 \cdot 2} = \dfrac{2}{3}\left(\dfrac{2}{2}\right)$ and, by the fundamental principle of fractions, $\dfrac{2}{3}\left(\dfrac{2}{2}\right) = \dfrac{2}{3}$.

Similarly, $\dfrac{8}{10} = \dfrac{4 \cdot 2}{5 \cdot 2} = \left(\dfrac{4}{5}\right)\left(\dfrac{2}{2}\right) =$ _____ .

497. An alternative form for writing

$\dfrac{4}{6} = \dfrac{2 \cdot 2}{3 \cdot 2} = \dfrac{2(2)}{3(2)} = \dfrac{2}{3}$ is $\dfrac{\overset{2}{\cancel{4}}}{\underset{3}{\cancel{6}}} = \dfrac{2}{3}$, where the slant bar

indicates that the numerator and denominator have each been divided by the common factor_____ .

$$\frac{-3a + 3}{4}$$

You first have
$$\frac{a + 1 - 2(2a - 1)}{4}.$$

338. The difference $\dfrac{a + 1}{4} - \dfrac{2a - 1}{2}$ is equal to the sum $\dfrac{a + 1}{4} + \dfrac{-(2a - 1)}{2}$. This last sum, when written as a single fraction, is _____ .

$$\frac{2a - 1}{3} + \frac{-(a + 4)}{4}$$

339. The difference $\dfrac{2a - 1}{3} - \dfrac{a + 4}{4}$ equals the sum _____ + _____ .

$$\frac{5a - 16}{12}$$

You first have
$$\frac{4(2a - 1) - 3(a + 4)}{12}$$

340. The sum $\dfrac{2a - 1}{3} + \dfrac{-(a + 4)}{4}$ can be written as the single fraction _____ . (Write the fraction in simplest form.)

$$\frac{3a + 4}{7} + \frac{-(2a - 1)}{2}$$

341. The difference $\dfrac{3a + 4}{7} - \dfrac{2a - 1}{2}$ can be written as the sum _____ + _____ .

$$\frac{-8a + 15}{14}$$

342. Write $\dfrac{3a + 4}{7} + \dfrac{-(2a - 1)}{2}$ as a single fraction in simplest form.

$$\frac{-3a + 14}{20}$$

343. Write the difference $\dfrac{a + 2}{4} - \dfrac{2a - 1}{5}$ as a single fraction in simplest form.

30

344. The LCD of the fractions in $\dfrac{a - 1}{2} - \dfrac{a - 3}{5} + \dfrac{a + 3}{3}$ is _____ .

$x - 5 + \dfrac{3}{2x + 3}$

487. Write the quotient and remainder in the preceding frame in the form of a polynomial plus a fraction.

$$(-12 + 2x^2 - 7x) \div (2x + 3) = \underline{\hspace{3cm}}.$$

Remark. So much for the division of one polynomial by another. The process you have learned is quite general and can be used to complete such examples as $x^2 - 3x \overline{)\,x^3 + 2x^2 - x + 1}$ or $x^3 - 2x^2 + 2x \overline{)\,x^5 - x^3 + 2x + 1}$. Although the process you have learned in the last sequence of frames is quite general, in many cases where the dividend is exactly divisible by the divisor, the quotient can better be represented in fractional form and then common factors can be divided from the numerator and denominator. Thus, $(x^2 + 3x + 2) \div (x + 1)$ can be looked upon as

$$
\begin{array}{r}
x + 2 \\
x + 1 \overline{)\,x^2 + 3x + 2} \\
\underline{x^2 + x} \\
2x + 2 \\
\underline{2x + 2}
\end{array}
$$

or as $\dfrac{x^2 + 3x + 2}{x + 1} = \dfrac{(x + 2)(x + 1)}{x + 1} = x + 2.$

Let us now turn back to the principal concern of this unit, fractions. We have already discussed the addition of fractions, and we shall next consider the products of fractions.

$\dfrac{6}{35}$

488. Recall that the product of two fractions

$$\left(\frac{a}{b}\right)\left(\frac{c}{d}\right) = \frac{ac}{bd}.$$

Thus, $\dfrac{2}{3} \cdot \dfrac{1}{5} = \dfrac{(2)(1)}{(3)(5)} = \dfrac{2}{15}$ and $\dfrac{3}{7} \cdot \dfrac{2}{5} = \dfrac{(3)(2)}{(7)(5)} = \underline{\hspace{2cm}}.$

$\dfrac{3}{8}$

489. $\dfrac{3}{4} \cdot \dfrac{1}{2} = \underline{\hspace{2cm}}.$

$\dfrac{4x}{3y}$

490. $\dfrac{x}{3} \cdot \dfrac{4}{y} = \underline{\hspace{2cm}}.$

$\dfrac{19a + 33}{30}$

345. $\dfrac{a-1}{2} - \dfrac{a-3}{5} + \dfrac{a+3}{3} =$

$\dfrac{(15)}{(15)}\dfrac{(a-1)}{2} + \dfrac{-(6)}{(6)}\dfrac{(a-3)}{5} + \dfrac{(10)}{(10)}\dfrac{(a+3)}{3} =$

$\dfrac{15a - 15 - 6a + 18 + 10a + 30}{30} =$ _____.

24

346. The LCD of the fractions in

$\dfrac{3a+1}{3} + \dfrac{a+2}{2} - \dfrac{a-3}{8}$ is_____.

$\dfrac{33a + 41}{24}$

347. Write $\dfrac{3a+1}{3} + \dfrac{a+2}{2} - \dfrac{a-3}{8}$ as a single

fraction in lowest terms.

Remark. While you have now learned to add fractions with unlike denominators, none of the fractions with which you have worked have had variables in the denominators. These we shall look at next. Before beginning, remember that we have already made the assumption that no variable in a denominator will assume a value for which the denominator will be equal to 0.

x^4

348. The LCD of a set of fractions contains as a factor each different factor occurring in any of the denominators, and it includes each factor the greatest number of times it occurs in any single denominator. For example, the LCD of $\dfrac{1}{x}$ and $\dfrac{1}{x^3}$ is x^3. The LCD of $\dfrac{1}{x}$ and $\dfrac{1}{x^4}$ is_____.

x^2

349. The LCD of $\dfrac{3}{x}$ and $\dfrac{2}{x^2}$ is_____.

$\dfrac{3x + 2}{x^2}$

350. $\dfrac{3}{x} + \dfrac{2}{x^2}$ equals $\dfrac{(x)3}{(x)x} + \dfrac{2}{x^2}$. Write this sum as a single fraction with the common denominator x^2.

Remark. This process is really not very hard to learn if you keep mentally comparing it with long division in arithmetic, with which you are already familiar.

$3x + 2;\ 2$

$$
\begin{array}{r}
3x\ +\ 2 \\
2x\ +\ 7\ \overline{)\ 6x^2\ +\ 25x\ +\ 16} \\
\underline{6x^2\ +\ 21x} \\
4x\ +\ 16 \\
\underline{4x\ +\ 14} \\
2
\end{array}
$$

482. Divide $6x^2 + 25x + 16$ by $2x + 7$. The quotient is _____ and the remainder is _____ .

$x + 3\ \overline{)5x^2 + 14x - 3}$

483. In dividing a polynomial by a binomial, both the polynomial and the binomial should be written in descending powers of the variable. Thus, the first step in dividing $14x - 3 + 5x^2$ by $3 + x$ is to set the problem up as

$$
\overline{)} \ .
$$

$5x - 1;\ 0$

$$
\begin{array}{r}
5x\ -\ 1 \\
x\ +\ 3\ \overline{)\ 5x^2\ +\ 14x\ -\ 3} \\
\underline{5x^2\ +\ 15x} \\
-\ x\ -\ 3 \\
\underline{-\ x\ -\ 3} \\
0
\end{array}
$$

484. Divide $14x - 3 + 5x^2$ by $3 + x$. The quotient is _____ and the remainder is _____ .

$2x - 1;\ 0$

You first have

$6x + 5\ \overline{)\ 12x^2 + 4x - 5}$

485. Divide $4x + 12x^2 - 5$ by $5 + 6x$. The quotient is _____ and the remainder is _____ .

$x - 5;\ 3$

You first have

$2x + 3\ \overline{)\ 2x^2 - 7x - 12}$

486. Divide $-12 + 2x^2 - 7x$ by $2x + 3$. The quotient is _____ and the remainder is _____ .

$4x^3$

$\dfrac{10x + 3}{4x^3}$

xy

$\dfrac{5 - 3x}{xy}$

$\dfrac{4 - 5xy}{x^2 y}$

$6x^2 y^2$

$\dfrac{4xy + 24y - 6x}{6x^2 y^2}$

$\dfrac{x^2 + x + 1}{x^3}$

You first have

$\dfrac{(x^2)}{(x^2)} \dfrac{1}{x} + \dfrac{(x)}{(x)} \dfrac{1}{x^2} + \dfrac{1}{x^3}.$

351. The LCD of the fractions in $\dfrac{5}{2x^2} + \dfrac{3}{4x^3}$ is _____.

352. $\dfrac{5}{2x^2} + \dfrac{3}{4x^3} = \dfrac{(2x)}{(2x)} \dfrac{5}{2x^2} + \dfrac{3}{4x^3} = $ _____.

353. The LCD of the fractions in $\dfrac{5}{xy} - \dfrac{3}{y}$ is _____.

354. $\dfrac{5}{xy} - \dfrac{3}{y} = \dfrac{5}{xy} + \dfrac{-(x)}{(x)} \dfrac{3}{y} = $ _____.

355. Write $\dfrac{4}{x^2 y} - \dfrac{5}{x}$ as a single fraction.

356. The LCD of the fractions in $\dfrac{2}{3xy} + \dfrac{4}{x^2 y} - \dfrac{2}{2xy^2}$ is _____.

357. $\dfrac{2}{3xy} + \dfrac{4}{x^2 y} - \dfrac{2}{2xy^2} = $

$\dfrac{(2xy)}{(2xy)} \dfrac{(2)}{(3xy)} + \dfrac{(6y)}{(6y)} \dfrac{(4)}{(x^2 y)} + \dfrac{-(3x)}{(3x)} \dfrac{(2)}{(2xy^2)} = $

_____.

358. Write $\dfrac{1}{x} + \dfrac{1}{x^2} + \dfrac{1}{x^3}$ as a single fraction.

$x - 6; \quad 0$

$$
\begin{array}{r}
x - 6 \\
x + 2 \overline{\smash{\big)}\ x^2 - 4x - 12} \\
\underline{x^2 + 2x} \\
-6x - 12 \\
\underline{-6x - 12} \\
0
\end{array}
$$

$x + 9; \quad 0$

$$
\begin{array}{r}
x + 9 \\
x - 2 \overline{\smash{\big)}\ x^2 + 7x - 18} \\
\underline{x^2 - 2x} \\
9x - 18 \\
\underline{9x - 18} \\
0
\end{array}
$$

$x - 3; \quad 1$

$$
\begin{array}{r}
x - 3 \\
x + 7 \overline{\smash{\big)}\ x^2 + 4x - 20} \\
\underline{x^2 + 7x} \\
-3x - 20 \\
\underline{-3x - 21} \\
1
\end{array}
$$

$x - 3 + \dfrac{1}{x + 7}$

$2x - 1; \quad 0$

$$
\begin{array}{r}
2x - 1 \\
3x + 2 \overline{\smash{\big)}\ 6x^2 + x - 2} \\
\underline{6x^2 + 4x} \\
-3x - 2 \\
\underline{-3x - 2} \\
0
\end{array}
$$

477. Divide $x^2 - 4x - 12$ by $x + 2$. The quotient is _____ and the remainder is_____ .

478. Divide $x^2 + 7x - 18$ by $x - 2$. The quotient is _____ and the remainder is_____ .

479. Divide $x^2 + 4x - 20$ by $x + 7$. The quotient is _____and the remainder is_____ .

480. Express the quotient and remainder in the preceding frame as a polynomial plus a fraction.

$$(x^2 + 4x - 20) \div (x + 7) = \underline{\hspace{3cm}}.$$

481. Divide $6x^2 + x - 2$ by $3x + 2$. The quotient is _____ and the remainder is_____ .

$$\frac{x^2 - x - 1}{x^3}$$

359. Simplify $\frac{1}{x} - \frac{1}{x^2} - \frac{1}{x^3}$.

$$\frac{yz + xz - xy}{xyz}$$

360. Simplify $\frac{1}{x} + \frac{1}{y} - \frac{1}{z}$.

$$\frac{11y^2 - 8}{8xy^2}$$

361. Simplify $\frac{3}{8x} - \frac{2}{2xy^2} + \frac{1}{x}$.

Remark. If any fractions in a sum have binomial (two-term) denominators, the problem of finding the least common denominator of the fractions is a little more complicated. The next few frames will consider this problem.

$3(x - 1)$

362. The LCD of the fractions $\frac{1}{2}$ and $\frac{1}{x + 2}$ is $2(x + 2)$, because this is the simplest common multiple of the two denominators. The LCD of $\frac{1}{3}$ and $\frac{1}{x - 1}$ is_____.

$x(x - 5)$

363. The LCD of the fractions in $\frac{3}{x - 4} + \frac{1}{x}$ is $x(x - 4)$, because this is the simplest common multiple of the two denominators. The LCD of the fractions in $\frac{4}{x - 5} + \frac{2}{x}$ is_____.

$6x(x - 1)$

364. The LCD of $\frac{1}{2x}$ and $\frac{3}{6(x + 2)}$ is $6x(x + 2)$. The LCD of $\frac{3}{3x}$ and $\frac{1}{6(x - 1)}$ is_____.

$4x(x + 1)$

365. The LCD of $\frac{5}{2x}$ and $\frac{6}{4(x + 1)}$ is_____.

$$x - 5 \overline{)\begin{array}{r} 2x \;+\; 3 \\ 2x^2 - 7x - 16 \\ \underline{2x^2 - 10x} \\ 3x - 16 \end{array}}$$

472. Divide the first term in the divisor, x, into $3x$, and write the resulting quotient in the appropriate place.

$$x - 5 \overline{)\begin{array}{r} 2x \\ 2x^2 - 7x - 16 \\ \underline{2x^2 - 10x} \\ 3x - 16 \end{array}}$$

$$x - 5 \overline{)\begin{array}{r} 2x \;+\; 3 \\ 2x^2 - 7x - 16 \\ \underline{2x^2 - 10x} \\ 3x - 16 \\ 3x - 15 \end{array}}$$

473. Multiply $x - 5$ by 3 and write the product in the appropriate place.

$$x - 5 \overline{)\begin{array}{r} 2x \;+\; 3 \\ 2x^2 - 7x - 16 \\ \underline{2x^2 - 10x} \\ 3x - 16 \end{array}}$$

$$x - 5 \overline{)\begin{array}{r} 2x \;+\; 3 \\ 2x^2 - 7x - 16 \\ \underline{2x^2 - 10x} \\ 3x - 16 \\ 3x - 15 \\ \underline{ - 1} \end{array}}$$

474. Subtract $3x - 15$ from $3x - 16$ and write the result in the appropriate place.

$$x - 5 \overline{)\begin{array}{r} 2x \;+\; 3 \\ 2x^2 - 7x - 16 \\ \underline{2x^2 - 10x} \\ 3x - 16 \\ 3x - 15 \end{array}}$$

$2x + 3;\; -1$

475. Since -1 is of lower degree than $x - 5$, the division process is completed. The quotient when $2x^2 - 7x - 16$ is divided by $x - 5$ is_____ and the remainder is_____.

remainder; divisor

476. If desired, the quotient can be expressed in the form of a polynomial plus a fraction. Thus,

$$(2x^2 - 7x - 16) \div (x - 5) = 2x + 3 + \frac{-1}{x - 5},$$

where the numerator of the fraction $\dfrac{-1}{x - 5}$ is the _____ and the denominator is the _____.

$6x(x-4)$

366. The LCD of $\dfrac{3}{2x}$ and $\dfrac{7}{3x(x-4)}$ is _____ .

$(x-2)(x-1)$

367. Sometimes more than one fraction in an expression contains a binomial denominator. For example, $\dfrac{3}{x+1} + \dfrac{2}{x-1}$ contains two fractions with different binomial denominators. The LCD of the fractions in $\dfrac{3}{x+1} + \dfrac{2}{x-1}$ is $(x+1)(x-1)$. The LCD of the fractions in $\dfrac{5}{x-2} + \dfrac{3}{x-1}$ is _____ .

$(x-4)(2x-1)$

368. The LCD of $\dfrac{3}{x-4}$ and $\dfrac{5}{2x-1}$ is _____ .

$x(x-1)(x+2)$

The factor x must be here, because neither $x-1$ nor $x+2$ is a multiple of x.

369. The LCD of the fractions in $\dfrac{2x-1}{x+2} + \dfrac{3}{x-1} + \dfrac{1}{x}$ is _____ .

$x(x-2)(x-3)$

370. The LCD of the fractions in $\dfrac{3x-1}{x-2} + \dfrac{5}{x(x-3)} + \dfrac{7}{x}$ is _____ .

Remark. Having learned to find the LCD for a set of fractions having binomial denominators, you are ready to return to the study of the addition of fractions. Be sure you read each frame carefully and concentrate on the meaning of the symbolism.

$2(x+3)$

371. The LCD of the fractions in $\dfrac{1}{2(x+3)} + \dfrac{3}{x+3}$ is _____ .

$2x$

467. To divide $2x^2 - 7x - 16$ by $x - 5$, the problem is first arranged

$$x - 5 \overline{)2x^2 - 7x - 16}.$$

When the first term in the dividend $(2x^2)$ is divided by the first term in the divisor, x, the result is _____.

$$\begin{array}{r} 2x \\ x - 5 \overline{)2x^2 - 7x - 16} \end{array}$$

468. Write the partial quotient $2x$ in the appropriate place.

$$x - 5 \overline{)2x^2 - 7x - 16}$$

$$\begin{array}{r} 2x \\ x - 5 \overline{)2x^2 - 7x - 16} \\ 2x^2 - 10x \end{array}$$

469. Multiply $x - 5$ by $2x$ and write the product in the appropriate place.

$$\begin{array}{r} 2x \\ x - 5 \overline{)2x^2 - 7x - 16} \end{array}$$

$$\begin{array}{r} 2x \\ x - 5 \overline{)2x^2 - 7x - 16} \\ \underline{2x^2 - 10x} \\ 3x \end{array}$$

You simply add the negative of $2x^2 - 10x$.

470. Subtract $2x^2 - 10x$ from $2x^2 - 7x$ and write the difference in the appropriate place.

$$\begin{array}{r} 2x \\ x - 5 \overline{)2x^2 - 7x - 16} \\ 2x^2 - 10x \end{array}$$

$$\begin{array}{r} 2x \\ x - 5 \overline{)2x^2 - 7x - 16} \\ \underline{2x^2 - 10x} \\ 3x - 16 \end{array}$$

471. "Bring down" -16 and write it in the appropriate place.

$$\begin{array}{r} 2x \\ x - 5 \overline{)2x^2 - 7x - 16} \\ \underline{2x^2 - 10x} \\ 3x \end{array}$$

$$\frac{7}{2(x + 3)}$$

You first have
$$\frac{1}{2(x + 3)} + \frac{(2)}{(2)} \frac{3}{(x + 3)} \cdot$$

372. Write $\dfrac{1}{2(x + 3)} + \dfrac{3}{x + 3}$ as a single fraction.

$3(x - 2)$

373. The LCD of the fractions in $\dfrac{1}{3(x - 2)} - \dfrac{2}{x - 2}$ is _____ .

$$\frac{-5}{3(x - 2)}$$

374. Write $\dfrac{1}{3(x - 2)} - \dfrac{2}{x - 2}$ as a single fraction.

$4(x - 2)$

375. The LCD of the fractions $\dfrac{1}{(x - 2)} + \dfrac{3}{4}$ is

_____ .

$$\frac{3x - 2}{4(x - 2)}$$

376. $\dfrac{1}{x - 2} + \dfrac{3}{4} = \dfrac{(4)\ (1)}{(4)(x - 2)} + \dfrac{(x - 2)(3)}{(x - 2)(4)} =$

$$\frac{4 + 3x - 6}{4(x - 2)} = \underline{\hspace{2cm}} \cdot$$

$4(x + 2)$

377. The LCD of the fractions in $\dfrac{3x}{4(x + 2)} - \dfrac{1}{2}$ is _____ .

$$\frac{x - 4}{4(x + 2)}$$

378. Write $\dfrac{3x}{4(x + 2)} - \dfrac{1}{2}$ as a single fraction.

$$\frac{4x - 11}{6(x - 2)}$$

379. Write $\dfrac{2}{3} - \dfrac{1}{2(x - 2)}$ as a single fraction.

464. The difference, $-x$, is written as shown,

$$\begin{array}{r} 3x \phantom{{}+8x-3} \\ x + 3 \overline{)\, 3x^2 + 8x - 3} \\ \underline{3x^2 + 9x} \\ -\,x \end{array}$$

and -3 is "brought down" to give

$$\begin{array}{r} 3x \phantom{{}+8x-3} \\ x + 3 \overline{)\, 3x^2 + 8x - 3} \\ \underline{3x^2 + 9x} \\ -\,x - 3 \end{array}$$

The entire process is now repeated. The trial divisor, x, is divided into the first term of $-x - 3$. The quotient of $-x$ divided by x is _____.

0

465. The quotient of $-x$ divided by x, -1, is written above the term $-x$, and is then multiplied by the entire divisor, $x + 3$, to yield $-x - 3$, which is written as shown.

$$\begin{array}{r} 3x - 1 \\ x + 3 \overline{)\, 3x^2 + 8x - 3} \\ \underline{3x^2 + 9x} \\ -\,x - 3 \\ \underline{-\,x - 3} \end{array}$$

When $-x - 3$ is subtracted from the terms immediately above, the remainder is _____.

does

466. When $3x^2 + 8x - 3$ is divided by $x + 3$, the quotient is $3x - 1$ and the remainder is 0. To check, $x + 3$ can be multiplied by $3x - 1$ to see whether the product of the two equals the dividend. $(x + 3)(3x - 1)$ (does/does not) equal $3x^2 + 8x - 3$.

Remark. Is it clear that this procedure is essentially the same in its mechanics as that involved in arithmetic long division? You divide, multiply, subtract, and "bring down"; divide, multiply, subtract, and "bring down"; and keep this up until you have a remainder that is of lower degree than the divisor.

$(x + 1)(x - 2)$

380. The LCD of the fractions in

$\dfrac{2}{x + 1} + \dfrac{3}{x - 2}$ is_____.

$\dfrac{5x - 1}{(x - 2)(x + 1)}$

381. $\dfrac{2}{x + 1} + \dfrac{3}{x - 2} =$

$\dfrac{(x - 2)\ (2)}{(x - 2)(x + 1)} + \dfrac{(x + 1)\ (3)}{(x + 1)(x - 2)} =$

$\dfrac{2x - 4 + 3x + 3}{(x - 2)(x + 1)} =$ _____.

$2(x + 1)$

382. The LCD of a set of fractions can be determined most easily when the denominators are written in factored form. For example, $\dfrac{1}{2x + 2} + \dfrac{3}{x + 1}$ equals $\dfrac{1}{2(x + 1)} + \dfrac{3}{x + 1}$. The LCD of the fractions is_____.

$\dfrac{7}{2(x + 1)}$

383. Write $\dfrac{1}{2(x + 1)} + \dfrac{3}{x + 1}$ as a single fraction.

$\dfrac{1}{3(x - 1)} - \dfrac{7}{6(x - 1)}$

384. Rewrite $\dfrac{1}{3x - 3} - \dfrac{7}{6x - 6}$ as an equal expression in which the denominators are in completely factored form.

$6(x - 1)$

385. The LCD of the fractions in

$\dfrac{1}{3(x - 1)} - \dfrac{7}{6(x - 1)}$ is_____.

$\dfrac{-5}{6(x - 1)}$

386. Write $\dfrac{1}{3(x - 1)} - \dfrac{7}{6(x - 1)}$ as a single fraction.

The next digit in the dividend, 5, is written beside 30, and the process is repeated yielding

$$
\begin{array}{r}
35 \\
61\,\overline{)\,2135} \\
183 \\
\hline
305 \\
305 \\
\hline
000
\end{array}
$$

6 is contained 5 times in 30

Product of 5 and 61
No remainder

$3x$

To find this number you can ask "By what must I multiply x to obtain $3x^2$?"

461. The procedure used in dividing 2135 by 61 is identical to that used to divide $3x^2 + 8x - 3$ by $x + 3$. The first step in this latter problem is to write

$$x + 3\,\overline{)\,3x^2 + 8x - 3}$$

and then to divide the trial divisor, x, into the first term of the trinomial, $3x^2$. The result of this division is_____.

$3x^2 + 9x$

462. The partial quotient, $3x$, is then written directly above $3x^2$ as shown.

$$
\begin{array}{r}
3x \\
x + 3\,\overline{)\,3x^2 + 8x - 3}
\end{array}
$$

Following this, $3x$ is multiplied by the entire divisor, $x + 3$. The product of $3x$ and $x + 3$ is_____.

$-x$

Remember, to subtract $3x^2 + 9x$ from $3x^2 + 8x$, add the negative of $3x^2 + 9x$ to $3x^2 + 8x$.

463. The result of multiplying $3x$ and $x + 3$ is then written directly beneath the first two terms of the dividend as shown.

$$
\begin{array}{r}
3x \\
x + 3\,\overline{)\,3x^2 + 8x - 3} \\
3x^2 + 9x
\end{array}
$$

The expression $3x^2 + 9x$ is then subtracted from $3x^2 + 8x$, which results in_____.

$\dfrac{3}{x} + \dfrac{2}{x(x-1)}$

387. Rewrite $\dfrac{3}{x} + \dfrac{2}{x^2 - x}$ as an equal expression in which the denominators are in completely factored form.

$x(x-1)$

388. The LCD of the fractions in $\dfrac{3}{x} + \dfrac{2}{x(x-1)}$ is_____.

$\dfrac{3x-1}{x(x-1)}$

389. Write $\dfrac{3}{x} + \dfrac{2}{x(x-1)}$ as a single fraction.

$x(x+3)$

390. The LCD of the fractions in $\dfrac{2}{x^2 + 3x} - \dfrac{1}{x+3}$ is_____.

$\dfrac{2-x}{x(x+3)}$

391. Write $\dfrac{2}{x(x+3)} - \dfrac{1}{x+3}$ as a single fraction.

$\dfrac{7}{4(2x-1)}$

Did you first have
$\dfrac{7x}{4x(2x-1)}$?

392. Write $\dfrac{5x}{4x^2 - 2x} - \dfrac{3x}{8x^2 - 4x}$ as a single fraction.

$\dfrac{6x+4}{3x(x+1)}$

393. Write $\dfrac{2}{3x+3} + \dfrac{4}{3x}$ as a single fraction.

$\dfrac{2x-4}{x(x+2)}$

394. Write $\dfrac{4x}{x^2 + 2x} - \dfrac{2}{x}$ as a single fraction.

$3x^2 - x + \dfrac{2}{x}$

456. Divide $6x^3 - 2x^2 + 4$ by $2x$.

You might first have
$\dfrac{6x^3}{2x} - \dfrac{2x^2}{2x} + \dfrac{4}{2x}$.

$2y^2 - 3y + \dfrac{5}{y}$

457. Divide $8y^3 - 12y^2 + 20$ by $4y$.

$-2z^2 + z - \dfrac{3}{z}$

458. $(10z^3 - 5z^2 + 15) \div (-5z) =$ _____ .

You might first have
$\dfrac{10z^3}{-5z} - \dfrac{5z^2}{-5z} + \dfrac{15}{-5z}$.

$-4y^3 - 3y^2 + \dfrac{1}{y}$

459. $(8y^4 + 6y^3 - 2) \div (-2y) =$ _____ .

$-x + 2y - \dfrac{1}{2}$

460. Divide $(4x^2y - 8xy^2 + 2xy)$ by $-4xy$.

Remark. A division problem somewhat similar to those we have been considering is that concerning division by a binomial. The process used is more complicated, however, and is comparable to the long-division algorithm of arithmetic.

We illustrate one example in detail to review the process in arithmetic before discussing similar division involving algebraic expressions.

Recall that to divide 2135 by 61, the symbolism $61\overline{)2135}$ is used and the complete algorithm appears as

$$\begin{array}{r} 3 \\ 61\overline{)2135} \\ \underline{183} \\ 30 \end{array}$$

6 is contained 3 times in 21 (6 is trial divisor)
Product of 3 and 61
Difference of 213 and 183

$\dfrac{5x + 4}{x(x + 1)}$

$\dfrac{5}{3(2x - 1)}$

You first have
$\dfrac{5x}{3x(2x - 1)}$, which
reduces to the form
shown.

$\dfrac{6}{3x + 1}$

You first have
$\dfrac{6x}{x(3x + 1)}$.

$\dfrac{2}{3(2x - 1)}$

395. Write $\dfrac{3x}{x^2 + x} - \dfrac{2}{x + 1} + \dfrac{4}{x}$ as a single fraction.

396. Write $\dfrac{3x}{2x^2 - x} - \dfrac{4}{6x - 3}$ as a single fraction.

397. Write $\dfrac{4x}{3x^2 + x} + \dfrac{2}{3x + 1}$ as a single fraction.

398. $\dfrac{4}{2x - 1} - \dfrac{3x}{2x^2 - x} - \dfrac{1}{6x - 3} = $ _____ .

Remark. Be sure that you do not go too rapidly through the frames here. The symbolism used must be read carefully if you are to follow the ideas being presented. In many of these frames, the symbols speak louder than words!

We shall now consider more complicated fractions. The methods used to add these fractions are exactly the same as those used with the fractions you have studied previously.

$y(y + 2)(y + 3)$

The order of the factors is not important.

399. Recall that the LCD of a set of fractions contains as a factor each different factor occurring in any of the denominators, and it includes each factor the greatest number of times it occurs in any single denominator. For example, the LCD of the fractions in $\dfrac{3}{x} + \dfrac{2}{(x + 1)(x + 2)} + \dfrac{3}{(x + 2)}$ is $x(x + 1)(x + 2)$. The LCD of the fractions in $\dfrac{4}{y} - \dfrac{3}{(y + 3)(y + 2)} + \dfrac{1}{(y + 2)}$ is _____ .

$-7y^2 + 6$

451. $(7y^4 - 6y^2) \div (-y^2) = $ _____.

$-4x^2 + 2x - 1$

452. Divide $16x^4 - 8x^3 + 4x^2$ by $-4x^2$.

Remark. Thus far, all of the division problems we have studied were quotients that could be represented by polynomials with integer coefficients. Sometimes, however, the quotient is not expressible in this form. That is, sometimes there is a "remainder."

$x + 5 + \dfrac{3}{x}$

You first have
$\dfrac{x^2}{x} + \dfrac{5x}{x} + \dfrac{3}{x}$.

453. To divide $x^2 - 3x + 2$ by x, the fraction $\dfrac{x^2 - 3x + 2}{x}$ can be written $\dfrac{x^2}{x} - \dfrac{3x}{x} + \dfrac{2}{x}$, and, when each term is simplified, the result is $x - 3 + \dfrac{2}{x}$, where the last term is a fraction. Divide $x^2 + 5x + 3$ by x.

$5x + 2;\ 3$

454. Dividing $2x^2 + 3x + 5$ by x results in $2x + 3 + \dfrac{5}{x}$, where the expression $(2x + 3)$ can be viewed as the "quotient," while 5 is viewed as a "remainder." Similarly, when $5x^2 + 2x + 3$ is divided by x, the "quotient" is _____ and the remainder is _____ .

Remark. In the preceding frame we used the word "quotient" to describe a partial quotient. There should not be any confusion in using the word in this sense.

$7x + 2 - \dfrac{1}{x}$

455. Instead of using the terms "quotient" and "remainder" in discussing the division process, it is better to think of $(3x^2 - 5x + 4) \div x$ either as $\dfrac{3x^2 - 5x + 4}{x}$ or as $3x - 5 + \dfrac{4}{x}$. Similarly, $(7x^2 + 2x - 1) \div x$ can be expressed as $\dfrac{7x^2 + 2x - 1}{x}$ or as

_____ .

$(x + 1)(x + 1)$

$x + 1$ must be included twice because it occurs twice in one of the denominators.

400. The LCD of the fractions in
$$\frac{2}{x + 1} + \frac{3}{(x + 1)(x + 1)} \text{ is} \underline{\hspace{3cm}}.$$

$(x - 1)(x + 1)(x + 1)$

401. The LCD of the fractions in
$$\frac{2}{x - 1} + \frac{3}{(x - 1)(x + 1)} + \frac{1}{(x + 1)(x + 1)}$$
is$\underline{\hspace{3cm}}$.

$(x - 1)(x - 1)(x + 2)(x + 2)$

402. The LCD of the fractions in
$$\frac{3}{(x - 1)(x - 1)} + \frac{2}{x + 2} - \frac{5}{(x + 2)(x + 2)}$$
is$\underline{\hspace{3cm}}$.

$x^2(x - 1)(x + 1)(x + 1)$

403. The LCD of the fractions in
$$\frac{2}{x^2} + \frac{3}{x(x + 1)(x + 1)} + \frac{1}{x - 1}$$
is$\underline{\hspace{3cm}}$.

$(x - 1)(x + 1)(x + 1)$

404. To find the LCD for the fractions in
$$\frac{3}{x^2 - 1} + \frac{2}{x^2 + 2x + 1}, \text{ it is first necessary to}$$
factor each denominator. Thus,
$$\frac{3}{x^2 - 1} + \frac{2}{x^2 + 2x + 1} = \frac{3}{(x - 1)(x + 1)} + \frac{2}{(x + 1)(x + 1)}.$$
The LCD for the fractions in the sum
is$\underline{\hspace{3cm}}$.

$(x + 1)(x + 2)$

405. $\dfrac{1}{x + 1} + \dfrac{2}{x^2 + 3x + 2}$ equals

$\dfrac{1}{x + 1} + \dfrac{2}{(x + 1)(x + 2)}.$ The LCD of the

fractions is$\underline{\hspace{3cm}}$.

$4x^2 - 6x - 10; \ 2$

444. The division of $11x^3 - 2x^2 + 3x$ by x can be accomplished by simply dividing each term in $11x^3 - 2x^2 + 3x$ by x. $4x^2 - 6x - 10$ can be divided by 2 by dividing each term in _____ by ____ .

$2x^2 - 3x - 5$

445. When $4x^2 - 6x - 10$ is divided by 2, the result is _____ .

$2x^2 - 3x - 9$

446. Divide $12x^2 - 18x - 54$ by 6.

$y^2 + 4y + 3$

447. $(3y^3 + 12y^2 + 9y) \div 3y =$ _____ .

Remark. There are three ways to look at a problem such as $(3y^3 + 12y^2 + 9y) \div 3y$. First, you can view it as a matter of reducing a fraction to lowest terms, $\dfrac{3y^3 + 12y^2 + 9y}{3y} = \dfrac{3y(y^2 + 4y + 3)}{3y} = y^2 + 4y + 3$; second, you can write the quotient as the sum of three terms, $\dfrac{3y^3}{3y} + \dfrac{12y^2}{3y} + \dfrac{9y}{3y}$, and then reduce each term to lowest terms to obtain $y^2 + 4y + 3$; third, you can mentally divide $3y$ into each term in $3y^3 + 12y^2 + 9y$ and arrive at the same result, $y^2 + 4y + 3$. The best way to view such a problem is a matter of individual preference. In short, you do what seems easiest to you.

$6x^2 - 3x + 1$

448. $(12x^2 - 6x + 2) \div 2 =$ _____ .

$2 - 4x - 5x^2$

449. $(6 - 12x - 15x^2) \div 3 =$ _____ .

$-15x + 7$

450. Divide $15x^3 - 7x^2$ by $-x^2$.

You might first have
$\dfrac{15x^3}{-x^2} + \dfrac{-7x^2}{-x^2}$

$$\frac{x + 4}{(x + 1)(x + 2)}$$

406. $\dfrac{1}{x + 1} + \dfrac{2}{(x + 1)(x + 2)} =$

$\dfrac{(1)\ (x + 2)}{(x + 1)(x + 2)} + \dfrac{2}{(x + 1)(x + 2)} =$

$\dfrac{x + 2 + 2}{(x + 1)(x + 2)} = \underline{\hspace{3cm}}$.

$$\frac{3}{x - 2} + \frac{4}{(x - 1)(x - 2)}$$

407. Rewrite $\dfrac{3}{x - 2} + \dfrac{4}{x^2 - 3x + 2}$ as an equal expression in which the denominators are in completely factored form.

$$(x - 1)(x - 2)$$

408. The LCD of the fractions in $\dfrac{3}{x - 2} + \dfrac{4}{(x - 1)(x - 2)}$ is $\underline{\hspace{3cm}}$.

$$\frac{3x + 1}{(x - 1)(x - 2)}$$

You first have
$\dfrac{3(x - 1) + 4}{(x - 1)(x - 2)}$.

409. Write $\dfrac{3}{x - 2} + \dfrac{4}{(x - 1)(x - 2)}$ as a single fraction.

$$(x + 3)(x - 2)$$

410. The LCD of the fractions in $\dfrac{2}{x + 3} - \dfrac{3x}{x^2 + x - 6}$ is $\underline{\hspace{3cm}}$.

$$\frac{-x - 4}{(x + 3)(x - 2)}$$

You first have
$\dfrac{2(x - 2) - 3x}{(x + 3)(x - 2)}$.

411. Write $\dfrac{2}{x + 3} - \dfrac{3x}{(x + 3)(x - 2)}$ as a single fraction.

$$\frac{2x + 12}{(x + 4)(x + 3)}$$

412. Write $\dfrac{4}{x + 4} - \dfrac{2x}{x^2 + 7x + 12}$ as a single fraction. (First determine the LCD.)

$x - 1$

439. Simplifying $\dfrac{x^2 - x}{x}$ can be looked at two ways, as a matter of reducing a fraction, and as a matter of dividing $x^2 - x$ by x. Recall that to reduce $\dfrac{x^2 - x}{x}$ to lowest terms, the common factor x can be factored from each term in the numerator; the fraction can first be written $\dfrac{x(x - 1)}{x}$ and then_____.

$x - 1$

440. To divide $x^2 - x$ by x, the quotient $\dfrac{x^2 - x}{x}$ can be written $\dfrac{x^2}{x} - \dfrac{x}{x}$, and each term in the latter expression can then be reduced to lowest terms. The result is_____.

$x^2 - 2x + 3$

441. To divide $3x^2 - 6x + 9$ by 3, the quotient $\dfrac{3x^2 - 6x + 9}{3}$ can be written $\dfrac{3x^2}{3} - \dfrac{6x}{3} + \dfrac{9}{3}$ and each term of this expression can then be simplified. The result is_____.

$2x^2 - 3x - 5$

$\dfrac{4x^2 - 6x - 10}{2} =$

$\dfrac{4x^2}{2} - \dfrac{6x}{2} - \dfrac{10}{2}$.

442. Divide $4x^2 - 6x - 10$ by 2.

$11x^2 - 2x + 3$

$\dfrac{11x^3 - 2x^2 + 3x}{x} =$

$\dfrac{11x^3}{x} - \dfrac{2x^2}{x} + \dfrac{3x}{x}$.

443. Divide $11x^3 - 2x^2 + 3x$ by x.

$$\frac{-x + 4}{(x - 1)(x - 5)}$$

413. Write $\dfrac{3x}{x^2 - 6x + 5} - \dfrac{4}{x - 5}$ as a single fraction.

$$(x - 1)(x + 2)(x - 3)$$

The order of the factors is not important.

414. $\dfrac{3}{x^2 + x - 2} + \dfrac{4}{x^2 - x - 6}$ equals

$\dfrac{3}{(x + 2)(x - 1)} + \dfrac{4}{(x - 3)(x + 2)}$. The LCD of the fractions in this expression is _____.

$$\frac{7x - 13}{(x - 1)(x + 2)(x - 3)}$$

415. $\dfrac{3}{(x + 2)(x - 1)} + \dfrac{4}{(x - 3)(x + 2)} =$

$\dfrac{(3)\quad(x - 3)}{(x - 1)(x + 2)(x - 3)} + \dfrac{(x - 1)\quad(4)}{(x - 1)(x + 2)(x - 3)} =$

$\dfrac{3x - 9 + 4x - 4}{(x - 1)(x + 2)(x - 3)} =$

$$\frac{1}{(x + 1)(x + 4)} + \frac{3}{(x + 1)(x + 2)}$$

416. Rewrite $\dfrac{1}{x^2 + 5x + 4} + \dfrac{3}{x^2 + 3x + 2}$ as an equal expression in which the denominators are in completely factored form.

$$(x + 1)(x + 2)(x + 4)$$

417. The LCD of the fractions in

$\dfrac{1}{x^2 + 5x + 4} + \dfrac{3}{x^2 + 3x + 2}$ is _____.

$$\frac{4x + 14}{(x + 1)(x + 2)(x + 4)}$$

418. Write $\dfrac{1}{x^2 + 5x + 4} + \dfrac{3}{x^2 + 3x + 2}$ as a single fraction.

$$(x - 2)(x - 3)(x - 3)$$

419. The LCD of the fractions in

$\dfrac{3}{x^2 - 5x + 6} + \dfrac{1}{x^2 - 6x + 9}$ is _____.

$\dfrac{y}{2}$

433. Since $\dfrac{a}{c} + \dfrac{b}{c} = \dfrac{a+b}{c}$, by the symmetric law,

$\dfrac{a+b}{c} = \dfrac{a}{c} + \dfrac{b}{c}$. Similarly, $\dfrac{x+y}{2} = \dfrac{x}{2} + $ _____ .

$\dfrac{5y}{3} + \dfrac{7}{3}$

434. The fraction $\dfrac{2x+3}{5}$ can be written as the sum

of two fractions, $\dfrac{2x}{5} + \dfrac{3}{5}$, where each fraction has the

denominator 5. Similarly, $\dfrac{5y+7}{3} = $ _____ .

$\dfrac{5x}{7} - \dfrac{11}{7}$

435. The fraction $\dfrac{3x-7}{2}$ can be written as the

difference of two fractions, $\dfrac{3x}{2} - \dfrac{7}{2}$, where each

fraction has the denominator 2. Similarly,

$\dfrac{5x-11}{7} = $ _____ .

$\dfrac{5y^2}{2} - \dfrac{7y}{2} + \dfrac{3}{2}$

436. The fraction $\dfrac{2x^2 - 7x + 9}{5}$ can be written

$\dfrac{2x^2}{5} - \dfrac{7x}{5} + \dfrac{9}{5}$. Similarly,

$\dfrac{5y^2 - 7y + 3}{2} = $ _____ .

$\dfrac{3x^2}{5} - \dfrac{2x}{5} + \dfrac{7}{5}$

437. $\dfrac{3x^2 - 2x + 7}{5}$ can be written as an expression

containing three fractions, _____ .

$x^2 - x; \ x$

438. A fraction is a representation of a quotient. $\dfrac{x}{y}$ means the quotient of x divided by y, and $\dfrac{x^2-x}{x}$ means the quotient of _____ divided by _____ .

$$\frac{4x - 11}{(x - 2)(x - 3)(x - 3)}$$

You first have
$$\frac{3(x - 3) + 1(x - 2)}{(x - 2)(x - 3)(x - 3)}.$$

420. Write $\dfrac{3}{x^2 - 5x + 6} + \dfrac{1}{x^2 - 6x + 9}$ as a single fraction.

$(x + 2)(x + 2)$

421. The LCD of the fractions in
$$\frac{2}{x^2 + 4x + 4} - \frac{3}{x + 2} \text{ is } \underline{\hspace{2cm}}.$$

$$\frac{-3x - 4}{(x + 2)(x + 2)}$$

422. $\dfrac{2}{x^2 + 4x + 4} - \dfrac{3}{x + 2} =$
$$\frac{2}{(x + 2)(x + 2)} + \frac{-(x + 2)(3)}{(x + 2)(x + 2)} =$$

$$\frac{2 - 3x - 6}{(x + 2)(x + 2)} = \underline{\hspace{2cm}}.$$

$(x - 1)(x + 1)$

423. The LCD of the fractions in
$$\frac{3}{x^2 - 1} - \frac{2}{x - 1} \text{ is } \underline{\hspace{2cm}}.$$

$$\frac{1 - 2x}{(x - 1)(x + 1)}$$

424. Write $\dfrac{3}{x^2 - 1} - \dfrac{2}{x - 1}$ as a single fraction.

$(x - 3)(x + 3)(x + 3)$

425. The LCD of the fractions in
$$\frac{2}{x^2 - 9} - \frac{4}{x^2 + 6x + 9} \text{ is } \underline{\hspace{2cm}}.$$

$$\frac{-2x + 18}{(x - 3)(x + 3)(x + 3)}$$

426. Write $\dfrac{2}{x^2 - 9} - \dfrac{4}{x^2 + 6x + 9}$ as a single fraction.

$$\frac{-3x + 5}{(x - 2)(x + 5)}$$

$$\frac{x^2 + 4x}{(x + 2)(x - 4)}$$

$$\frac{x^2 + x - 3}{(x - 3)(x + 3)}$$

$$\frac{-x^2 + 3x + 2}{(x + 1)(x + 6)}$$

$$\frac{-x^2 + 13}{(x + 3)(x - 4)}$$

$$\frac{-2x + 2}{(x - 2)(x + 3)}$$

427. $\dfrac{x + 1}{x^2 + 3x - 10} + \dfrac{x - 2}{x + 5} =$

$$\frac{x + 1}{(x - 2)(x + 5)} + \frac{(x - 2)(x - 2)}{(x - 2)(x + 5)} =$$

$$\frac{x + 1 + x^2 - 4x + 4}{(x - 2)(x + 5)} = \underline{\qquad\qquad} .$$

428. Write $\dfrac{x - 2}{x^2 - 2x - 8} + \dfrac{x + 1}{x - 4}$ as a single fraction.

429. Write $\dfrac{x + 1}{x + 3} + \dfrac{3x}{x^2 - 9}$ as a single fraction.

430. $\dfrac{2x}{x^2 + 7x + 6} - \dfrac{x - 2}{x + 6} =$

$$\frac{2x}{(x + 1)(x + 6)} + \frac{-(x + 1)(x - 2)}{(x + 1)(x + 6)} =$$

$$\frac{2x - (x^2 - x - 2)}{(x + 1)(x + 6)} = \frac{2x - x^2 + x + 2}{(x + 1)(x + 6)} = \underline{\qquad\qquad} .$$

431. $\dfrac{4}{x^2 - x - 12} - \dfrac{x - 3}{x - 4} =$

$$\frac{4}{(x + 3)(x - 4)} + \frac{-(x + 3)(x - 3)}{(x + 3)(x - 4)} .$$ Simplify the sum of the two fractions.

432. Write $\dfrac{x^2 - 3x}{x^2 + x - 6} - \dfrac{x + 1}{x + 3}$ as a single fraction.

Remark. You are now able to add fractions. In fact, you can now add fractions with some fairly complicated denominators. Before looking at the operations of multiplication and division with fractions, we want to use part of what you have learned to this point and look at the problem of dividing one polynomial by another.